THIS BOOK BELONGS TO

Jacob's dream

STORIES FROM THE OLD TESTAMENT

STORIES FROM
THE
OLD TESTAMENT

This edition published 1995 by Longmeadow Press,
201 High Ridge Road, Stamford, CT 06904.

Cover and interior design by Geddes and Grosset Ltd.

ISBN 0 681 10514 3

Printed and bound in Slovenia.

First Longmeadow Press Edition

0 9 8 7 6 5 4 3 2 1

CONTENTS

LIST OF PLATES

IN THE BEGINNING

Six Wonderful Days

The first story in the Bible tells how God made the world in six wonderful days. Each day He made some new and lovely thing. On the first day He made light; on the second day, blue skies and seas; on the third day, the mountains, hills and meadows, the trees, the grass, and the flowers; on the fourth day, the golden sun, the moon and the stars; and on the fifth day He made the fishes and the lovely birds; then on the sixth day He made all the animals, great and small; and last of all, God created Adam, the first man.

In His own image God made him, and breathed the breath of life into him. He called the man Adam, and He made him able to think, to be happy, and to enjoy the wonderful world God had given to him to live in; He also made him lord of all the living creatures on the earth, the beasts and birds, the fish and the creeping things.

So the heaven and the earth were finished, and all the living creatures upon the earth.

And God saw everything that He had made, and behold, it was very good.

The Garden of Delight

Then the Lord God made a garden in a place called Eden, which is a name that means "delight". In the garden God planted every tree that is pleasant to the sight and good for food. And in the midst of the garden He set two mysterious trees—the Tree of Life, and the Tree of the Knowledge of Good and Evil.

It was the most beautiful place there has ever been in the world; and God gave the garden to Adam, to dress it and to keep it. Adam was very happy there, for in that lovely place was neither anger nor fear, neither sorrow nor pain, but only love and joy, peace and happiness.

All the animals and birds came to Adam in friendliness, quite unafraid, and Adam gave to each a name. "And whatever Adam called every living creature, that was the name thereof."

And God Himself came, and talked with Adam. He told him that the garden was for his pleasure, and that he might eat and enjoy the fruit of every tree that grew there except the fruit of the Tree of the Knowledge of Good and Evil. That, said God, he must never eat or touch, or he would die.

One day, God made Adam fall into a deep sleep, and while he was sleeping, God made a companion for him, so that he should never be lonely in the garden. This was Eve, created to be Adam's wife, friend and companion, to share his life and all the good and wonderful things God had given to him.

When Adam awoke, Eve was beside him. He looked at her in wonder—Adam had never seen one of his own kind before. Eve smiled at him; Adam smiled at Eve, and they loved one another. Happily they wandered hand in hand through the garden, while Adam eagerly showed Eve all its beauties, all its marvels. He took her to see the mysterious Tree of the Knowledge of Good and Evil, and told her what God had said of it. And when God came to them in the cool evening, they ran joyfully to meet Him, for God was their Friend.

Now among the animals in the garden was a serpent, and he was very sly and cunning. Lurking among the bushes, he watched Adam and Eve, and saw all that they did, and how they never ate from the strange tree, and into his mind came a mischievous thought.

One day he came upon Eve alone, picking fruit in the sunshine, and he asked her why she did not eat of the forbidden tree. Eve told him what God had said of it, that if they touched its fruit they would die.

But the wily serpent said, "Of course you will not die. You will only become clever and wise, as wise as God Himself, knowing both good and evil." And he tempted her, until at last Eve put out her hand and plucked the forbidden fruit. It was, as the serpent had said, lovely to eat, and she ran with some to Adam, that he also might become clever and wise. And Adam ate of it too.

The wicked serpent slithered away.

But Adam and Eve, standing in the garden, stared at one another. When would they begin to feel wise and wonderful? But they did not feel wise and wonderful at all; they felt guilty and ashamed and troubled. They knew they had disobeyed God, Who had given them so much, and only asked one thing of them. Looking guiltily at one another, they knew evil, misery and shame. They had known only goodness and beauty before.

They fled away and hid themselves among the trees of the garden.

When God came to them in the evening, they did not go running joyfully to meet Him; they were *afraid*. Never before had they known fear.

But God, of course, knew what they had done. He called until they came at last, shamed and miserable. God was very grieved. Sorrowfully He told them their punishment.

They might no longer stay in the beautiful garden, but must go away, out into the world beyond the gates. There Adam would have to work hard, tilling the rough ground for food. They would have to bear, God told them, hunger and pain, sickness and sorrow, and at last death. For now they knew evil as well as good, and evil brought all these things with it, and death came to those who ate of the forbidden tree, as He had told them.

So hand in hand, in sorrow and shame, Adam and Eve fled from the grief and anger of God, out into the world beyond the gates, never to enter it again.

And God set angels at the gates, and a fiery sword which turned every way, to keep the way of the Tree of Life.

But though God banished them from the garden, He did not cease to love and care for them. Though He was grieved, He forgave them, provided them with food and clothing, and gave them happiness of another kind. Though they could never be as happy again as at first in that beautiful garden, they knew that God was still watching over them and caring for them.

The People of the Tents

The stories in the Bible tell us of people who lived, thousands of years ago, in the land we now call Palestine. Some of these people built great cities, with fine palaces and temples and houses. They made beautiful things, too, with their hands: carvings in ivory, gold and silver ornaments, and fine pottery.

There were other people, too, who built no cities, nor houses to live in, but wandered from place to place, living in tents. They were shepherds, with flocks of sheep and goats, and herds of cattle. Some of them were proud chieftains, and very rich in silver and gold, as well as flocks and herds. But the greatest treasure of the people of the tents was their belief in and love of, the true God. The people in the cities worshipped things they could *see*—the sun or the moon; or they made gods for themselves of wood or stone, and built great temples for their worship. But the shepherd folk worshipped the one true God; though they could not see Him, they had faith in Him. All their stories were of God, all their songs and poems. The little children round the campfire in the evenings were told of Him, and learnt to love Him.

The stories in the Bible are the stories of these shepherd people of the tents. Sometimes they did wrong, sometimes they forgot God's commands; but always, whether they were fighting, or whether they were prisoners in a far country, or whether they had returned to live in cities of their own in the Promised Land, they remembered and believed in the one true God.

God had given to Abraham a promise that through his descendants all the nations of the earth should be blessed. Though they did not understand it, that promise was precious to them, and it came true when Jesus was born in Bethlehem, to bring God's message of love and peace to all the nations of the world.

The Great Flood

Through the long years after Adam and Eve left the Garden of Eden, the earth became peopled with great numbers of men and women, knowing both good and evil, as Adam and Eve had known. Everyone was able to choose in his heart which he would follow, the right or the wrong. But as the years went on, more and more people forgot God and chose to do evil in His sight. They became cruel and wicked, their hearts were filled with greed and hatred; they knew neither love nor kindness. God was grieved and angry to see the beautiful world He had created so filled with wickedness. And He said, "I will destroy man whom I have created from the face of the earth; both man, and beast, and the creeping thing, and the fowls of the air; for I am sorry that I have made them."

But there was one man who loved God, and who chose to do good and not evil. His name was Noah, and Noah was "a just man, and perfect, and Noah walked with God". So God would not destroy Noah with the evil men. He talked to him, and told him what He meant to do—to send a terrible flood to destroy all living things upon earth. But God promised that Noah and his family should be saved, and He told Noah to build an ark of wood, like a great ship. He was to make rooms in it, and to cover it with pitch, inside and out, that it might be quite watertight. It was to be built in three storeys, with a door in the side, and a window above, and a roof over all.

Noah and his family leave the ark

Abraham and Isaac go up the mountain

And God told Noah that with him into the ark he was to take seven of every living creature that was good for food, and two of every other kind. And besides the animals Noah was to put in food, great quantities of all kinds, enough to feed people and animals for a long time.

What a task that was! But Noah did all that God had said. The animals were gathered together, the food harvested and stored in the ark, and when God warned Noah that the time had come, Noah shepherded all the creatures, two by two, into the great ship. Then he and his family entered too, and the door was shut.

Then the sky turned dark. The winds rose, the thunder roared, lightning flashed, and the rains began. Faster and faster the rain beat down, day after day, night after night. Great tides roared in from the seas, the rivers burst their banks, the waters rose higher and higher, swallowing up houses, trees, hills and mountains, until they covered the whole earth. All the frightened animals, the birds and the creeping things on the earth were drowned with the frightened people who had been so wicked. Only the great ark floated safely upon the waters.

For forty days and nights the rain continued. Noah, looking out, could see nothing at all but water, grey water like a great sea, heaving and tossing under a grey sky.

But after many days the clouds fled away, the sun shone warmly out, and God sent a wind to help to dry the earth. How glad Noah and his family were to see the sun once more! And then one day the tops of the mountains appeared. Noah was pleased, for he knew then that the waters were really going down at last. He fetched a raven, opened the window and set the bird free. Off into the sunshine, rejoicing to use his wings once more, the raven flew, and he did not come back to the ark.

Noah took a dove, and sent her out also, but soon she was back again, fluttering at the window, for she could find no rest for the sole of her foot. Noah opened the window and took her in.

After seven days he sent the little bird out a second time. She stayed away all day, but at evening time she was back again, carrying an olive leaf in her beak. Noah knew then that the tops of the trees were uncovered at last.

After seven more days, the dove was sent out a third time. She returned no more, so Noah knew that the earth was swiftly drying up, and that the bird could find food and rest for herself again.

Then Noah and his sons removed the roof from the ark, and they saw that the earth was dry.

So at last Noah and his family left the ark they had lived

in for so long, and with them went all the other creatures. The animals and birds scattered joyfully in all directions over the green hills and valleys, glad and happy to leave the dark ark and be free once more. They ran and leaped and flew and crawled away, to make new homes and rear new families in peace and freedom.

Noah and his sons built an altar to the Lord God, a place where they might pray to Him and thank Him for all His goodness and kindness in saving them from the flood.

And God heard their thanks, and He made a promise to Noah and his sons, that never again would He send a great flood to destroy all living creatures; but, said God, "While earth remains, seed time and harvest, and cold and heat, and summer and winter, and day and night, shall not cease."

Then for a sign and token of His promise, God set a beautiful bow in the cloud. It was the first rainbow. And God told Noah that whenever He set the rainbow in the cloud He would remember His promise; and whenever men saw it they should remember it too.

The Friend of God

Hundreds of years had passed since Noah and his sons left the ark, and this story begins in a city beside the sea—a city called Ur of the Chaldees. In Ur lived a man who was a great chief, and his name was Terah. Now Terah was a descendant of Shem, one of Noah's sons—descendants are children, and grandchildren, and great-grandchildren—and Terah had three sons of his own, Abraham, Nahor, and Haran. Our story is about Abraham. When he was a boy his father and his brothers called him Abram, but later God changed his name to Abraham, so we will call him Abraham.

Abraham and his brothers grew up in Ur of the Chaldees. They walked in the narrow streets between the tall houses, where the laden camels passed on their way to the wharves beside the sea. They saw the tall-masted ships in the harbour, ships from faraway India or Egypt. Sometimes they would walk beside the great river that flowed into the sea at Ur, and see fields of grain and pleasant gardens. But wherever they went they could see, towering above the city, the great coloured temple with its gilded roof that was built for the worship of Nannar, the moon god. For the people of the world had once more forgotten God, and worshipped idols and all sorts of strange man-made images. At every new-moon tide the priests of Nannar made a great festival in the coloured temple, and all the people came to praise and give sacrifices, rejoicing that the moon god was rising once more from the darkness to bring them good fortune, as they thought.

Abraham, perhaps, went to these services, but as he grew up and became a man, his heart was not satisfied. He could not *believe* in this moon god. Somehow he felt that there was a God greater than sun or moon or stars—a God Who did not set like the sun, or change like the moon, Who was not cold and far away like the stars; but a living God, Lord of all heaven and earth, yet One Whom a man could love, to Whom he could talk as a friend.

One day Terah, Abraham's father, told him he had decided to leave the city of Ur and go into a land called Canaan. Abraham was to go with him, and Sarai, Abraham's wife, and Lot, who was Terah's grandson, the son of Haran, who had died in Ur.

So one day a great procession set out from Ur of the

Chaldees. At the head rode Abraham, wearing a long, flowing cloak, and a white head-cloth, bound about with a rope of camel's hair. Abraham rode on a tall riding camel, and behind him Terah, who was an old man then, rode on a litter, or bed. Lot and Sarai, riding with her women, came next, and after them a long procession of servants and slaves, men, women and children; shepherds and dogs, with flocks of sheep and goats, and herds of cattle; and asses and camels laden with all Terah's goods and riches.

The procession moved slowly, keeping pace with the sheep and goats, who pattered along, following their shepherds. Each night the company halted; the slave women put up the black tents of goats'-hair cloth, while the menservants tended the animals. Soon everyone, fed and rested, slept beneath the stars.

For many days they travelled, until they came to a place called Haran. It was a long, weary journey for Terah to make, and when they reached Haran they stayed and settled in the city.

Now in Haran the people worshipped the moon god too, and some of them other gods, with many rites and ceremonies, some of them cruel and wicked.

And it was in Haran that Abraham heard God, the true and living God, speaking to him.

And God said to Abraham, "Get thee out of thy country, and from thy father's house, unto a land that I will show thee. And I will make of thee a great nation; and I will bless thee, and make thy name great; and thou shalt be a blessing. And I will bless them that bless thee, and curse him that curseth thee, and in thee shall all the families of the earth be blessed."

And Abraham, hearing and trusting, obeyed God and set out again from Haran. But before he went, Terah, his father, died. And Abraham mourned for him, and buried him there with all honour.

The Unburnt Offering

Abraham and Sarai dwelt in peace and were happy. Only one thing troubled them—they had no children of their own. It was true that Abraham had one son—his name was Ishmael, and Abraham loved him. But Ishmael was not Sarai's son; his mother was an Egyptian named Hagar.

Now God had promised Abraham that a son should be born to him and Sarai. Yet the years went on, and still no baby came to them. But Abraham trusted God's word, and at last, when he was nearly one hundred years old, God's promise came true, and a little son was born to him and Sarah, as Sarai was now known. They called him Isaac—a name which means "laughter", perhaps because of the joy in their hearts at his coming.

Isaac grew up tall and strong, a joy to his father and mother; a happy little boy, a member of a happy family, taught to love, trust and serve the God of his father, Abraham.

One night Abraham was lying awake in his cool, comfortable tent. All around was quiet—the quiet stars shone in the quiet sky, the tents stood quiet and peaceful in the starlight—the whole camp was asleep, except Abraham.

Suddenly, in the stillness, a voice spoke to Abraham, and the voice was the voice of God.

"Abraham!"

And Abraham answered, "Behold, here I am!"

Then God gave to Abraham a new and terrible command. "Take thy son, thine only son, whom thou lovest, and get thee into the land of Moriah; and offer him there for a burnt offering upon one of the mountains which I will tell thee of."

Abraham listened, and his heart filled with sorrow and

dismay. Abraham knew that the heathen people of Canaan quite often sacrificed their children to their gods of wood and stone. Now God, the true and living God, had asked the same hard thing of him. Sacrifice his son, his only son, the child he loved better than all the world! How could he do it?

But God had spoken, and never yet had Abraham failed to obey, and he knew he must obey even this dreadful command, and have faith that, in spite of it, God would be true to his promise.

So, as the sun peeped over the edge of the eastern hills, Abraham arose and went out into the lovely morning. He said nothing to Sarah, but saddled one of the asses and called two of his young men, bidding them get ready to go with him. Then he went to call his little son. Isaac awoke quickly, joyfully, glad to go out into the fresh morning, and ready for any journey.

First of all they went to cut wood, and when they had tied it into faggots, the little procession set off. Isaac ran about happily, chattering to his father of all the things he saw by the way. The road led them uphill, among grey rocks and through stony valleys. Here and there were patches of green, where the shy gazelles grazed; and as they climbed higher they saw wild goats leaping up the mountainsides. They saw holes in the rocks where the little foxes hid, and the jackals. Now and then they met a shepherd, leading his pattering flock to fresh pastures.

All these things interested Isaac, and the birds and the flowers beside the way, as he laughed and talked to his father. But Abraham was very quiet; he looked sad and stern, his thoughts on the terrible task before him.

On the third day of their journey, they came to a rough plain, and beyond the plain towered a mountain which Abraham knew was the place God meant for the sacrifice.

Here Abraham halted. He told his servants to wait for them, and he took the wood they had brought, and gave it to Isaac to carry. He himself took the small vessel holding the charcoal fire, and a knife, and they set off to climb the mountain.

Isaac walked lightly, eagerly, as though it were as easy to climb the mountain as to walk on the level plain. But as they went on the boy became troubled and perplexed. He knew they were on their way to make a burnt offering to God, but his father's silence and his sad, stern looks, made him feel that something must be very wrong. He fell silent himself. But presently he asked a question. "My father!" he said, and Abraham answered, "Here am I, my son." Then Isaac said, "Behold the fire and the wood, but where is the lamb for a burnt offering?"

Abraham said sadly, "My son, God will provide himself a lamb for a burnt offering." So they went on again in silence, and at last they came to the lonely top of Mount Moriah. There Abraham built an altar of the stones lying about, and he piled the wood around it. Still no lamb appeared, and Isaac looked at his father. Where *would* Abraham find a lamb for the sacrifice?

But at last he understood; for his father took him, and bound him, and laid him on the altar and the wood. Isaac looked at his father with pitiful eyes, but in silence, and Abraham turned his face away to hide the tears that were in his own eyes. But then he stretched out his hand and took the knife to slay his son. He raised his arm—the knife gleamed in the sun—but suddenly a voice from heaven cried, "Abraham! Abraham!"

Abraham lowered his arm. "Here am I!" he said.

Then the voice of the angel called again to him, "Lay not thine hand upon the lad, neither do thou anything unto him; for now I know that thou fearest God, seeing thou has not withheld thy son, thine only son, from me," and Abraham, listening, found that the tears in his eyes now were tears of gladness.

How joyfully he unbound Isaac, and how they rejoiced together and gave thanks to God! Then Abraham, hearing a struggling noise behind him, looked round, and there was a ram, caught in a thicket by its horns. So Abraham took the ram and offered it up instead of his son Isaac.

And when the sacrifice was over, the angel called again from heaven and told Abraham how pleased God was with him for his faith and obedience. Then the angel repeated the promise that God had made to him before, that his descendants should be as many as the stars in the sky.

GREAT MEN OF ISRAEL

The Brothers

Isaac married a beautiful girl called Rebekah, and some years afterwards Abraham died and was buried in the only piece of Canaan, the Promised Land, which he really owned. This was the field he had bought when his wife, Sarah, died; and in a cave in that field Isaac and his brother, Ishmael, buried their father beside his wife.

Isaac was then the great chief, owning all the riches of Abraham, the gold and silver, the flock and herds, and the tasselled spear of the chief stood upright beside *his* tent. The precious promise was his also, which God had given to Abraham, that the land of Canaan should belong to him and to his descendants, and that through him all the nations of the earth should be blessed.

Isaac and Rebekah had two sons, and they were twins.

Esau was the elder, and Jacob was the younger. Twins are often very like one another, but Esau and Jacob were quite different.

Esau was a brown boy, and hairy. He was very lively and active, not liking to sit still or be quiet, but happiest when out riding or hunting.

Jacob was a fair boy, smooth-skinned, quiet and thoughtful. When *he* grew up he liked best to stay with his father's shepherds and the flocks.

Isaac often talked to his boys of the wonderful promise of God, which would one day be passed on with his blessing to Esau. The promise and the blessing were the "birthright" of Esau—he would have them because he was the elder son.

The two boys would listen respectfully while their father was talking, but as soon as he finished, Esau forgot all about it. But Jacob, thoughtful and dreamy, during his quieter days in the fields thought of it often. It was so wonderful and precious, this promise that God had given to his father. Jacob dreamed of it every day; he wished with all his heart that the promise could be given to him, instead of to Esau, who cared nothing for it. No doubt Jacob talked to his mother about it, and Rebekah made up her mind that somehow Jacob should get his heart's desire, for Rebekah loved

Jacob far more than she loved happy-go-lucky Esau. But Esau was his father's favourite son.

One day Esau returned from hunting, tired and terribly hungry. Jacob was making some red lentil pottage for his own dinner, when Esau came staggering along, worn out and faint, and asked his brother to give him some of it to eat.

Then Jacob had a very mean idea. "Sell me this day thy birthright," he said, and Esau, who was feeling too tired to care about anything, answered, "Behold, I am at the point to die, and what profit shall this birthright do to me?"

Jacob wanted to make sure, so he still held back the food. "Swear to me this day," he said. And Esau promised, and so sold his birthright.

Then at last Jacob fed his brother with some of the lentil pottage and gave him bread also, and Esau ate and drank. Afterwards he felt much better and forgot all about his birthright.

But Jacob did not forget, and he now thought of himself as the elder son; and before his father died, he managed by deception to get from the blind old man the blessing that should have been Esau's. Esau was so angry that he threatened to kill Jacob; and Rebekah, his mother, who had planned the cruel trick, sent him for safety to Haran, where she had lived as a child.

We have to remember that Jacob, though guilty of these mean tricks, came later to have a great faith in God.

Jacob Dreams a Dream

Jacob set out quite alone on his long journey, only taking some food—bread and oil, dates and figs, and a skin bottle full of water to drink.

Before he went, his father had given him another blessing: "And God Almighty bless thee, and make thee fruitful, and multiply thee, that thou mayest be a multitude of people; and give thee the blessing of Abraham, to thee, and to thy seed with thee; that thou mayest inherit the land wherein thou art a stranger, which God gave unto Abraham."

So Jacob received from his father the wonderful promise of which he had dreamed so long. But as he went on his lonely way, hurrying from the anger of his brother, leaving his beloved home for a strange land, no doubt he thought about the wrong he had done and wondered whether God would forgive him.

One evening he found himself in a narrow, rocky valley. All around him bare hills rose to the starry sky. It was a

Jacob's dream

Joseph is sold as a slave

desolate, lonely spot, but if only he had known, it was very near the place where his grandfather, Abraham, had built an altar to God long ago, and called it Bethel. The darkness had come suddenly, as it does in the eastern countries. Jacob knew he could go no farther that night. He wrapped his cloak about him, set his food bag and water bottle beside him, and lay down to sleep with a stone for a pillow. Jacob was strong, and he was used to sleeping out of doors, used also to having a stone for his pillow, as the Arabs do even today, in that same wild countryside, so that he was soon fast asleep under the stars.

And as he slept he dreamed a wonderful dream.

He dreamed he saw a golden staircase reaching from earth to heaven, and on it bright angels passing up and down, so that the whole place shone with glory. And in his dream Jacob heard a voice from heaven speaking to him.

"I am the Lord God of Abraham thy father, and the God of Isaac; the land whereon thou liest, to thee will I give it, and to thy seed; and thy seed shall be as the dust of the earth, and thou shalt spread abroad to the west, and to the east, and to the north, and to the south, and in thee and in thy seed shall all the families of the earth be blessed. And, behold, I am with thee, and will keep thee in all places whither thou goest, and will bring thee again unto this land; for I will not leave thee until I have done that which I have spoken to thee of."

Jacob awoke and gazed about him. The shining golden staircase had gone, the angels were back in heaven. Only the stars shone brightly as before. But in his heart Jacob heard again those wonderful words, and knew that he had now received the promise from God Himself, as it had been given to Isaac, his father, and to Abraham.

And he said, "Surely the Lord is in this place; and I knew it not." He was awed and afraid, and he said to himself, "How dreadful is this place! This is none other but the house of God, and this is the gate of heaven." He slept no more that night; his thoughts were all of his wonderful dream, and as soon as the morning light appeared, Jacob arose. He took the stone he had used for a pillow and stood it upright. Then he poured oil upon it, making an altar as Abraham had done before him. His heart was full of wonder and praise to God, and he vowed to serve him always; and of all that God should give him, he vowed to use a tenth part in the service of God Himself.

Then he went on his lonely way, but in his heart was a feeling that now he was not alone, for God was with him; in spite of his wrongdoing, God had not forsaken him.

He came at last to Haran, and there he stayed with his Uncle Laban for many years. He worked for his uncle as a shepherd, and he married Laban's daughters, Leah and Rachel. Through the years he became rich, owning camels, flocks of sheep and goats, and herds of cattle. He had children, too, sons and daughters.

Joseph the Dreamer

Many years afterwards Jacob returned to Canaan, bringing his family with him, and his flocks and herds and other possessions. Esau met him, and the old quarrel was forgotten. Then Jacob went to Haran, where he found his father, Isaac, a very old man now, but so glad to meet Jacob once more and hear all his adventures.

When Isaac died, Esau came to Jacob, and they buried their father in the cave of Machpelah, where Sarah and Abraham and Rebekah lay.

Jacob had twelve sons, and two of them he loved more than all the others. These two were his younger sons, Joseph and Benjamin. Perhaps he loved them more because they were motherless and because they were Rachel's children, for Jacob had loved his wife Rachel with a very great and patient love.

Joseph was a handsome lad, eager and bright-eyed. His father was proud of him and, not very wisely, showed openly that Joseph was his dearest. This made his other sons jealous.

One day Jacob gave Joseph a new coat of many colours. When they saw it, his brothers became more angry and envious than ever. Perhaps it seems strange to be so jealous of a new coat for a younger brother, but this was a special coat. It was made of fine rainbow-coloured linen, and it was long, almost down to Joseph's feet; also it had long sleeves. The elder brothers, dressed as shepherds, wore sleeveless tunics with leather girdles, and over them they wore cloaks of camel hair. But Jacob, their father, wore a long coloured coat, with sleeves down to his wrists, like the coat he had given to Joseph. Only the chief, and his heir, wore such long, bright garments, so that when the brothers saw Joseph in his bright new coat, they knew that Jacob wished to make *him* the heir.

One night Joseph dreamed a dream. It was such a vivid dream he told it to his brothers. "Behold," he said, "we were binding sheaves in the field, and lo, my sheaf arose and stood upright; and behold, your sheaves stood round about and made obeisance to my sheaf."

His brothers were angrier than ever, for they thought Joseph was boastfully telling them that one day they would bow down before *him*. "Shalt thou indeed reign over us?" they said scornfully.

Soon afterwards Joseph dreamed another strange dream, and this time he told it to his father also. "Behold, I have dreamed a dream more," he said, "and behold, the sun and the moon and the eleven stars made obeisance to me."

Even his father rebuked him that time, but all the same Jacob remembered about the dream and thought about it often. He had taught all his sons to worship God and had tried to teach them the secret of friendship with Him, so that they might hear if God should speak to them. Joseph's father thought that God might have some special message for Joseph, some work for him to do, and that these dreams were God's way of speaking to him.

Joseph the Messenger

One day Jacob called Joseph and told him he wished him to go to his brothers, who had taken the flocks to pasture land at Shechem. "Go, I pray thee," he said, "see whether it be well with thy brethren and well with the flocks, and bring me word again."

Joseph set off cheerfully, but when he came at last to Shechem there were no black tents dotted about, no sheep, shepherds or dogs to be seen. The stone was rolled before the mouth of the well; the troughs were empty. Joseph wandered about until he met a stranger, who asked him kindly, "What seekest thou?"

When Joseph told him, the man said that his brothers had taken the flocks to fresh pastures at a place called Dothan. So Joseph set off again, and presently in the distance he could see the clustered tents, and the sheep and cattle grazing. He hurried on, eager to get news for his father, and to greet his brothers.

Now Joseph was wearing his bright new coat, so his

brothers saw him coming while he was yet afar off, and, "Behold," they mocked, "this dreamer cometh."

Then they made a wicked plot to kill him. "Let us slay him," they said, "and cast him into some pit, and we will say some evil beast hath devoured him; and we shall see what will become of his dreams!"

But Joseph's eldest brother, Reuben, was kinder than the rest, and he thought of his father and how grieved he would be if harm came to Joseph. So he persuaded the others not to kill Joseph but just to lower him into a pit. Reuben meant to come back later and rescue his young brother and take him home again.

Soon Joseph drew near, and came cheerfully to greet them all. But they seized him roughly, tore off his beautiful coat, and threw him into a pit near by. It was a deep hole, such as the shepherds would dig to catch rainwater. But this one was empty.

Then the brothers sat down to eat, and while they were eating, they looked up and saw, on the distant road, like a picture against the sky, a long procession of camels. These carried loads of spices and balm and myrrh, and the merchantmen to whom they belonged were Ishmaelites— grandsons and great grandsons of Ishmael, that son of Abraham who had become a mighty hunter and prince of the desert. These merchantmen travelled the road to Egypt, carrying spices and gums to sell there, and bringing back linen and cotton in return.

As the procession drew nearer, one of the brothers had a new idea. Instead of killing Joseph, they would sell him as a slave to these merchantmen. In this way they would not only get rid of their young brother but would receive money for him also, yet they would not be guilty of his death.

So they hauled Joseph out of the pit and sold him to the merchants for twenty pieces of silver, and he was carried off to Egypt to be sold again as a slave.

Then the cruel brothers killed a kid and dipped Joseph's coat in the blood, until it was stained most horribly. Afterwards they led their flocks back to Hebron, and taking the telltale coat to Jacob, told him they had found it beside the way.

Poor Jacob knew the coat instantly. He cried out in horror, "It is my son's coat; an evil beast hath devoured him; Joseph is no doubt rent in pieces," and he rent his garments and wept sorely for his dearest son, and refusing to be comforted, he mourned for many days.

Joseph in Egypt

And while his father mourned for him, Joseph was taken to faraway Egypt. Egypt at that time was a great and mighty empire. What a strange world it seemed to the boy from the tents, as he stood in the slave market, where the merchants had taken him to be sold! Here were great houses, with flower gardens and trees about them; here were temples, pyramids, tall pillars covered with strange marks, which he afterwards learned that men could read and understand; here were chariots and horses, and crowds of people dressed in clothes different from his own, speaking a language he had never heard before. How anxiously he watched and tried to understand what was said, as the bargaining for him went on! But Joseph, though wishing with all his lonely heart that he were once again with his loving old father, yet held his head proudly. God, he was sure, would not forsake him.

And God did not forsake him, though in Egypt Joseph had many strange adventures. He became a slave, he was made a prisoner through no fault of his own, he was lonely in a strange land. Yet through all his troubles he never forgot God, but learned patience and wisdom from Him. Then at last there came a time when, with God's help, he was able to be of great service to Pharaoh, the King of Egypt, and for this help he was made ruler over all the land, trusted and honoured by all men.

For God warned Pharaoh in a dream, which no one except Joseph could explain to him, that after seven years of good harvests a terrible famine would come upon Egypt, when for seven other years no food would grow in all the land. Joseph was able to advise Pharaoh how to prepare for this dreadful time by building great barns and storehouses, and saving food during the years of plenty.

So Pharaoh made Joseph a ruler over all Egypt, that Joseph himself might do all this work of preparation for him, and when the seven years of plenty ended Joseph had so much corn stored away that he could not count it.

When at last the famine came and the people were starving, they cried to Pharaoh for bread. He sent them to Joseph, telling them to obey him in all things. Then Joseph opened the great barns and sold corn to all the Egyptians.

Now the famine was not only in Egypt, but over all the earth. Away in Canaan Jacob and his sons were in great distress, so when Jacob heard that there was corn to be bought in Egypt, he sent his ten elder sons to buy. But Benjamin he would not send, lest harm should come to him.

So one day, as Joseph watched the selling of the corn in the marketplace, he saw ten men in the well-remembered dress of Hebrew shepherds, and he knew them at once! His brothers!

They came near and bowed humbly before him, not recognising in the great Egyptian ruler the young brother they had sold so long ago. Had they known him, how frightened they would have been! But Joseph, through the long years, had learned to forgive them, for he saw now that it was God Who had brought him to Egypt that he might do this great work for Him and save the people.

Yet, wishing to test his brothers, Joseph spoke roughly, accusing them of being spies, come to do mischief. They answered earnestly that they were no spies, but brothers, come only to buy corn, that one of their number was dead, and one at home with their father. But Joseph, still pretending, sent them to prison for three days. Then he went to them and said they might have the corn, but that one of them must stay in prison in Egypt until the others returned bringing their youngest brother with them.

In great distress, and thinking that the Governor could

not understand them, for he had spoken in Egyptian, the brothers talked together, saying that it was because they had treated Joseph so unkindly, and had not listened when he pleaded with them, that they were now in all this trouble.

But Joseph, of course, understood; he knew now that his brothers were really sorry for their cruelty, and he went away and wept.

When he returned to the prison he bound Simeon, and sent the others away, each with a sack of corn.

On the way home, one of them, stopping to feed his ass, was terrified to find in the mouth of his sack the money he had paid for the corn. He cried out, and when the others found that every sack had money in it, they were very worried.

At last they reached home and told Jacob the story. Jacob was much troubled. "Me ye have bereaved of my children," he mourned, "Joseph is dead, Simeon is gone, and ye will take Benjamin away!" and he refused to let Benjamin go.

But when the corn was all eaten, and the famine worse than ever, Judah persuaded his father to let Benjamin go, promising that he would answer for his safety with his own life.

So Jacob sent a fine present for the Governor, and told

his sons to take back all the money they had found in their sacks, and more beside, to pay for the corn they needed.

Once more the brothers stood before Joseph in the market place, and Joseph's heart rejoiced when he saw Benjamin with them. He ordered his servant to take them to his own house. Then they were much afraid, fearing they were to be accused of stealing, and they explained earnestly to the steward how they had brought back the first money, and more beside. However, the steward spoke kindly to them, and brought Simeon to them, so they felt a little happier.

Later, with the Governor himself, they sat down to a splendid feast, and Joseph sent them special dishes from his own table.

That night Joseph commanded his steward to fill sacks with corn for them, and to put back each man's money once more; also in Benjamin's sack he was to hide Joseph's own silver cup.

The next morning the brothers set off very happily— Simeon was with them, Benjamin was safe.

Soon, however, galloping hooves brought the steward riding after them, and he accused them of having stolen the Governor's own silver cup.

Of course they declared they had done no such thing, and they agreed that if the cup *were* found, the owner of that sack should return to Egypt to become a slave.

Then how terrible was their grief when the cup was found in Benjamin's sack! They rent their clothes, and said they would all return to Egypt.

When they reached Joseph's house once more, they knelt humbly before him, and Judah pleaded earnestly with him. He told how Jacob still mourned for Joseph, his son, and how much he loved Benjamin. He begged Joseph to let Benjamin go home and to keep him, Judah, as a slave in his place, for he was sure that if harm came to Benjamin, and they returned without him, his father would die.

Joseph could keep his secret no longer. He ordered everyone from the room except his brothers, and when he was alone with them he told them the truth, weeping.

"I am Joseph," he said. "Doth my father yet live?"

But his brothers just stared—they could not understand. So Joseph said again, "I am Joseph, your brother, whom ye sold into Egypt."

Then at last they knew him, and their faces showed their shame and fear.

But Joseph went on, "Now therefore, be not grieved nor angry with yourselves, that ye sold me hither, for God did send me before you to preserve life," and he told them all the story of his years in Egypt.

Then he put his arms round Benjamin and wept, and Benjamin wept with joy also to find his brother once again.

Then Joseph kissed all his brothers, and they talked together for a long time.

When Pharaoh heard that Joseph's brothers had come, he was very pleased. He told Joseph to send them to fetch his father, and their wives and children, that they might live in Egypt. For Joseph's sake they should have the best that the land could give them. They were to take wagons to carry the women and children, and stores of food and clothing.

So Joseph sent his brothers away with splendid presents for his father, and a special gift for Benjamin.

When the brothers reached home and told Jacob their story, he could not at first believe them. But when he saw the wagons, and the gifts Joseph had sent, the happy old man cried: "It is enough! Joseph my son is yet alive; I will go and see him before I die."

So Jacob and his family went to Egypt and dwelt there. And the number of them, children and grandchildren, was seventy. The little family of Abraham, which had been just Abraham, Sarah and Isaac, was growing. God had said that the descendants of Abraham should be a great nation. It was beginning to come true. God had also promised that the land of Canaan should be given to them. Now they had left Canaan and were living in Egypt. But a later story tells how that promise also came true; how, when the Children of Israel had grown into a great nation, they left Egypt and returned to the Promised Land.

Joseph reveals himself to his brothers

The finding of the infant Moses

THE STORY OF MOSES

The Cradle in the Reeds

For hundreds of years the descendants of Jacob lived peacefully in their tents in the land of Goshen, taking care of their flocks and herds, reaping their fields of corn, and gathering their fruit. They grew in numbers until the seventy people who came with Jacob had grown to many thousands.

Other Pharaohs reigned on the throne of Egypt. As long as Joseph's wise rule was remembered, and all he had done for Egypt, the Children of Israel were left in peace. But at last there came to the throne a cruel Pharaoh, who knew nothing of Joseph, and who became frightened when he saw what a great number of Israelites lived in part of his kingdom, people rich and clever, and worshipping a strange, unknown God. He was afraid that one day they might rise up against him. So he made the Hebrew men and women into slaves. They were forced to work very hard, and if they did not work hard enough, they were flogged with whips. The Hebrew men were made to make bricks, and their taskmasters treated them very, very cruelly. Yet still, in spite of suffering, such lots of bonny little boys and girls were born to them, and their numbers went on growing.

So Pharaoh thought they were still a danger, and he gave a new order. Every boy baby born to the Hebrews was to be thrown into the river Nile!

Now among the Hebrews was a man named Amram, who belonged to the family of Levi. He and his wife, Jochebed, lived among their own people in Goshen. They had a son, Aaron, and a daughter, Miriam. Then one day another little boy was born to them. For three months his mother managed to hide him; no one knew anything about him. But the baby grew fast, and at last his mother knew she could hide him no longer. So she made a plan.

She and Miriam went to the river and gathered numbers of tall papyrus reeds, and with them they made a little cradle, a cradle with a lid. When they had woven it, Jochebed covered it with pitch inside and out, which made it quite watertight.

When it was finished a cosy blanket went into it, and on the blanket Jochebed laid her baby son. She closed the lid, and then very carefully she and Miriam carried it to the edge of the river. And there, when no one was about, among the lotus flowers and flags, and the great tall reeds, Jochebed hid her cradle. It floated safely on the water, and inside the baby still slept peacefully. With a last sorrowful look, Jochebed turned away and left it there, and went back along the sandy road to her home again. But Miriam stayed to watch—no one would notice a little girl idling beside the river.

In the cool of the evening there came the sound of voices and footsteps, women's voices, soft and merry; and Miriam, peeping between the tall reeds, saw a lovely lady, a princess, walking with her maidens beside the river. The daughter of Pharaoh had come down to bathe. There, by the pool, where the flags and the stately palm trees grew, the princess halted, and while her maidens watched and guarded her, she prepared to enter the water. But suddenly she caught sight of the cradle among the reeds, and sent one of her maids to fetch it for her.

When it was brought, and the lid raised, the baby awoke, and seeing the strange faces about him, he began to cry. The Princess was kind and tenderhearted, and she felt sorry for the little one. "This is one of the Hebrews' children," she said, and she picked up the baby in her arms.

Anxious Miriam, who had seen everything, drew nearer

and nearer until she could hear as well as see. The Princess was saying that she would like to adopt the lovely baby but who would nurse him for her if she did?

Then brave Miriam, breathless and eager, drew nearer still and said to the Princess, "Shall I go and call a nurse of the Hebrew women, that she may nurse the child for thee?" And the Princess smiled at her, and said, "Go!"

Off ran Miriam, straight home, and brought back with her—Jochebed, her own mother.

Perhaps the kind Princess guessed that the little girl had fetched the baby's own mother, but all she said was, "Take this child away and nurse it for me, and I will give thee thy wages."

So the baby went back to his own home to be nursed and cared for. What a happy household that was that night! How Jochebed praised Miriam for her cleverness! The baby was quite safe now; no one would harm the adopted child of the daughter of the king.

When the little boy grew old enough to do without his mother's care, he was taken to the Princess, for she said that now he must be brought up as her son. And she called his name Moses, meaning "drawn out", "Because," she said, "I drew him out of the water."

Moses the Prince

So Moses lived in the palace and was brought up as a prince. He went to school and had the best education that any boy at that time could have, for in Egypt were schools and universities, and Moses had the finest teachers in the world. He grew up strong and wise, learning all the wisdom of the Egyptians. But though he lived among the Egyptians and enjoyed the luxuries of the court, he did not forget his own people, and when he was with his father and mother, he learned from them of the true God.

As he grew older Moses became aware that, though he himself was happy and fortunate, his own people were miserable. One day he went himself to the brick fields to see what went on, and he saw one of the taskmasters cruelly beating a poor overworked Hebrew. That made Moses so angry, he struck the Egyptian a terrible blow and killed him. No one had seen, he thought, so he buried the man in the sand, and went away.

But the next day he went again, and this time saw two of his own people fighting one another. When he tried to stop them, the man in the wrong said to him, "Who made thee a prince and a judge over us? Intendest thou to kill me as thou killest the Egyptian?"

So Moses knew that someone had seen what he had done the day before. He knew also that if Pharaoh heard of it, his life would be in danger, so he went away to a country called Midian.

Moses the Shepherd

In Midian Moses lived with the family of a man named Jethro, and he became a shepherd for him. Later on he married one of Jethro's daughters, named Zipporah.

So, no longer living the busy, luxurious life of a prince in a great city, Moses spent his days in lonely places among the hills, minding the flocks. And during those long, quiet days he thought of the poor Hebrew slaves left behind in Egypt. How could he help them? How could they be rescued? Killing the Egyptian had not helped. That way was of no use, but there must be a plan, only Moses could not see it. But God had a plan, and at the right time Moses learned of it.

For one day Moses, minding the flock near a high mountain, saw a strange sight. The plain around was dotted with thorn bushes, and suddenly one of them burst into flame. But though the bush was blazing, it did not burn away.

As Moses drew nearer to see this great sight, to his surprise he heard a voice from the burning bush calling, "Moses! Moses!"

Moses stood still, and answered, "Here am I!"

Then the voice from the bush said, "Draw not nigh hither; put off thy shoes from off thy feet, for the place whereon thou standest is holy ground; I am the God of thy father, the God of Abraham, the God of Isaac, and the God of Jacob."

Then Moses covered his face in awe. God told him that the time had come to rescue His people, the Children of Israel, from the Egyptians, and to bring them up out of Egypt to a good land, "a land flowing with milk and honey".

Moses was overjoyed when he heard this and knew that God had a plan. But when God went on to say that He wished Moses himself to go to Egypt to face Pharaoh and to bring out the Children of Israel from the land of bondage, Moses was dismayed and afraid. Why had God chosen him for this terribly hard task? He began to make excuses and to plead with God to send someone else.

But God promised that He would be with Moses to help him. For God knew that, in spite of his fears, Moses was so strong and wise and *faithful*, he was the *right* man to carry out His plan, and at last Moses set off for Egypt with his brother Aaron, who was to help him and to speak for him.

When the brothers stood bravely before Pharaoh and asked him to let the people go, they had no easy task. Pharaoh said, "Who is the Lord, that I should obey His voice? I know not the Lord, neither will I let Israel go." Pharaoh did not mean to part with all these useful slaves.

Then Moses did as God commanded and told Pharaoh that if he would not let the people go, terrible misfortunes would come upon him and upon his country; and so it came to pass. For God sent dreadful plagues upon Egypt—one after another— and when Pharaoh still remained stubborn and cruel, He sent one last, worst of all, disaster upon them. It was so dreadful that Pharaoh himself, as well as all his terrified people, urged the Children of Israel to hurry out of their country, giving them gold and silver and jewels, anything to get rid of them and all the misfortunes the Egyptians had borne because of them.

So early one morning, before it was light, the Children of Israel, with Moses and Aaron leading them, moved off in orderly ranks, thousands and thousands of them, with their families and their cattle and their goods, marching out of the land of Egypt to return to the land God had promised to Abraham.

Moses the Leader

How strange it must have seemed to the little children of the Hebrews, to be hurried away in such a great company almost before it was light. But they saw that their fathers and mothers were very glad about something, so they would be glad too, and enjoy the unusual bustle and excitement.

Moses led the people across a lonely wilderness towards the Red Sea. There were other ways they might have taken, but then they would have passed through the lands of other people, friends of the Egyptians, who might have fought with them, so this lonely road was better. And God set a pillar of cloud before them by day, and a pillar of fire by night, to show them the way to go. At last the long procession came to the shores of the Red Sea, and they camped there.

They had not been long beside the sea, however, when they became aware of the thundering of horses' hooves and chariot wheels behind them. Pharaoh, as soon as he realised that the Children of Israel had really gone, changed his mind once again; calling for all his horses and chariots, his horsemen and his army, he went after them in great haste, determined to bring them back to slavery again.

How frightened the Israelites were! There were mountains on one side of them, the sea in front of them, the Egyptians behind. How could they escape?

They cried out to Moses, blaming him for bringing them out of Egypt, only to die in the wilderness.

But Moses answered firmly, "Fear ye not, stand still, and see the salvation of the Lord, which He will show you today; for the Egyptians whom ye have seen today, ye shall see them again no more for ever. The Lord shall fight for you, and ye shall hold your peace."

Then God set the pillar of cloud *behind* the Children of Israel, so that it made a great darkness before the Egyptians, and they could not see the fugitives. But the pillar gave bright light by night to the Children of Israel.

Then Moses lifted up his rod and stretched out his hand over the sea, as God had commanded him. And God sent a strong wind that blew all night, driving the waters back on either hand, leaving a path of dry ground across the sea bed. And the Children of Israel marched safely over, between the walls of water, to the other side. Every one of them got safely across.

Pharaoh's army, his chariots and horsemen, came galloping after them, straight into the midst of the sea. But now they were in trouble, for their chariot wheels sank so deeply in the wet sand that they could not move them, do what they might. In the darkness they cried out in panic, "Let us flee from the face of Israel, for the Lord fighteth for them against the Egyptians."

But it was too late.

God told Moses to stretch forth his rod again over the sea. Moses did so, and the wild waters came rushing back with tremendous force, and before they could help themselves, all the hosts of Pharaoh were drowned.

So God saved the Children of Israel from their enemies that night, and in the morning they saw the Egyptians dead upon the seashore.

All the people rejoiced at their great deliverance, and they feared God and worshipped Him, and had faith in Moses their wise leader.

The Wayfarers

The Children of Israel were safely out of the land of bondage; there were no cruel taskmasters here to make their lives miserable. Moses, leading them on through the wilderness, was a great and splendid leader. It was no easy task to lead that great company through the hot, bare desert places, where often food was scarce and water not to be found. Moses was sure that God would provide for them. But the people were not so sure. Whenever they met with any trouble they muttered against Moses and against God. Over and over again they grumbled and refused to trust God, though over and over again they had proof of His love and care for them. When they were short of water, God told Moses how to find it for them. When they became short of food, He sent them "bread from heaven", the silvery manna that came with the falling dew, so that they could gather it afresh every morning. And many other signs and wonders God showed them through Moses, His friend and servant.

Some of the people, of course, were sincere and wise men and women, trusting God and their leader in everything. But others were so often faithless, selfish and disobedient. If only they would have trusted and served God truly, their whole journey might have been happy. They had to go slowly because of the children and the animals, but it was not really very far to the land of Canaan. But because they would not trust and obey God they had to learn many hard lessons.

All this was a great sorrow to Moses, and he often pleaded with God for them, that He would forgive them and turn away His anger from them. For though they vexed and disappointed him, Moses loved these people he had rescued from slavery. Moses was a brave man, noble and unselfish; he was a friend of God, as Abraham had been, and God loved him and helped him to become the great and splendid leader that he was.

One day the long procession reached a wide plain at the foot of a great cloud-capped mountain. Rocks and mountains were all round them, but the plain was fertile—there was food for the flocks and herds, and in among the rocks were green glades where trees grew and fruit and flowers. This was a splendid camping ground, so here they pitched their tents for many months. Wonderful things were to happen on the holy mount of God.

There came a day when thunder rolled, lightning flashed,

and over the mountain hung a thick dark cloud, and round about the darkness were smoke and fire. The mountain shook, and through all the noise of the thunder the terrified people heard the sound as of a trumpet.

Then out of the cloud came the voice of God calling to Moses to come up to Him on the mount. So Moses went up and disappeared into the cloud, while below the people watched in awe and wonder.

Up on the mountain God gave to Moses the ten commandments—the laws God wished the people to learn and to obey. God told Moses many other things also, rules of life and conduct He wished the people to follow.

When Moses came again down the mountain, he wrote down all the words of the Lord, and rising early in the morning he built an altar under the hill, and set round about it twelve pillars for the twelve tribes of Israel. Then he read out to the people all the wonderful words God had spoken to him, and the people offered on the altar sacrifices and peace offerings.

But again God wished to speak with Moses. So Moses took his young servant Joshua, and climbed again to the lonely mountain top, leaving Aaron in charge of the camp. Moses was gone forty days and forty nights.

Down on the plain the people waited. But when day after

day passed and their leader did not return, they grew very impatient. And in their impatience they committed a great sin.

Some of the people who came out of Egypt with Moses were not true descendants of Jacob, and living all their lives in Egypt, they remembered the gods of the Egyptians, the "sacred" bulls and cows, and they could not yet understand the true God—the Invisible. Though they had heard Moses read out God's command—"Thou shalt not make to thyself any graven image"—they still thought they wanted a god they could see.

So they brought gold ornaments to Aaron and forced him to make of them a golden image, a calf. And when it was set up they worshipped it with dancing and singing.

God saw what they were doing, and He was very angry. He told Moses what He saw, and Moses was aghast, but he pleaded for the disobedient ones and begged God to forgive them.

Yet when at last he and Joshua came down from the mountain, even before they could see the camp, they heard the noise of shouting and chanting, and Joshua said to his master, "There is a noise of war in the camp!"

But Moses knew it was not war, and they hurried on. Now Moses was carrying two tablets of stone on which were engraved the ten commandments which God had given to him. As they drew near the camp they saw what was happening, and Moses became so angry that he flung the tablets down, and they broke into pieces.

When the guilty people saw Moses returning, his eyes flashing with splendid wrath, they were terrified. They knew they had done a great wrong.

Moses threw down the golden calf and ground it to powder before their eyes, and he punished the wrongdoers severely; but when God threatened them with more punishment, Moses begged God to forgive them and not to forsake them, and at last God did forgive them.

And Moses went again up the mountain, and God replaced the broken tablets by two more.

Then Moses told the people of all the laws God had given to him. He told them, too, of the desire in his heart to build a splendid Tent of Meeting in God's honour, and he asked the people to help him. So joyfully and willingly they brought their gifts—gold and silver and jewels, skins and fine cloth, and embroideries in gorgeous colours. And they all helped to build a most beautiful House of God, which became their most precious possession, and was carried with them wherever they went.

Into the Promised Land

There was a great encampment on the banks of the River Jordan. Every night, the frightened people on the other side of the swollen river, looking across the water, saw hundreds of watch fires flaming far and wide against the dark sky. The watch fires belonged to the Children of Israel, for now between them and the Promised Land flowed only this river of Jordan. Once before they had reached the borders of Canaan, but they had had neither courage nor trust in God, so they had not been allowed to enter, but had to wander for forty years in the wilderness.

Now Moses was dead, and Joshua was their leader, and he knew that there would be hard fighting to do against the idol-worshippers of Canaan before the Children of Israel could possess the land. But God had given to Joshua a message: "Be strong, and of a good courage; be not afraid, neither be thou dismayed; for the Lord thy God is with thee whithersoever thou goest."

When they looked across the water and saw all those thousands of Israelites camped upon the banks, it was no wonder the people of Canaan were afraid. Joshua knew all about their fear, for he had sent two of his soldiers secretly to the city of Jericho to spy out the land. The soldiers slipped through the gates unnoticed, and all day they went about talking to the people and finding out the strength of the walls, and how they were guarded.

When night came they went to the home of a woman named Rahab, whose house was built upon the city wall. When the soldiers of the King of Jericho came hunting for them, Rahab hid them under the flax spread out to dry on the flat roof of her house. So the searchers found nothing. After dark Rahab took a scarlet cord, and she let the two men down outside the city wall, so that they could escape to their own camp. But before they went, the spies promised that when the Children of Israel took the city, Rahab and all her family should be saved from all harm. They told her to tie the scarlet cord in the window of her house, so that they would know it again.

One morning Joshua ordered the Children of Israel to get ready to march. Now it was the time of harvest and the river was flooded—it seemed impossible to cross. Nevertheless the people obeyed, and packed their tents and prepared to go.

Then first of all went the priests, bearing on their shoulders the beautiful Ark of the Covenant, the gold of it glittering in the sun. Some distance behind marched the soldiers and the people. As soon as the feet of the priests touched the water's edge, the river ceased to flow, and the water rose in a wall, as the waters of the Red Sea had done forty years before. The priests walked on until they stood firmly in the middle of the river bed. There they stayed, while all the people crossed safely over on dry land into the land of Canaan.

Then, while the priests still stood there, Joshua ordered twelve men to bring to him twelve large stones from the river bed, and when that had been done, the priests also came up into the new land. As soon as the golden Ark had passed over, the waters of the river returned in a flood. Then Joshua piled up the twelve great stones—one for each tribe of the people—as a memorial of that wonderful day.

In the Promised Land

The First Victory

The Children of Israel had safely crossed the Jordan into the Promised Land, but beyond the place where they were camping loomed the walled city of Jericho. Before they could go farther into the country this city must be conquered. So Joshua prayed, and God told him what to do.

The people of Jericho, terrified of the great army outside their walls, locked all the gates, and no one was allowed to go out or to come in.

Then one day the sentries on guard on the walls saw a strange sight, and thought surely the battle was about to begin. Around their city marched a long procession. First came a great army of soldiers, marching silently. Next came seven priests marching before the beautiful golden Ark of the Covenant, and the seven priests blew continually on seven trumpets of rams' horns. Behind the Ark and the

69

priests marched another army of silent soldiers. So they went once around the city walls and returned to their camp.

The next day the procession came again and marched as before, the soldiers silent, the priests blowing their trumpets before the Ark. Each day for six days the same thing happened.

But on the seventh day the Children of Israel rose as soon as it was light and marched around the walls not once, but seven times.

And as the soldiers marched round the seventh time, and the priests blew with their trumpets, Joshua gave the people an order: "Shout, for the Lord hath given you the city!"

So when they heard the sound of the trumpets, all the people shouted with a great shout, and at that tremendous sound the great walls of the city fell down flat, and the Children of Israel, marching each man straight before him, entered the city and possessed it.

Gideon

There came a sad time for the Children of Israel, when a new enemy appeared. They had settled down in peace to till the ground and keep their flocks, but during those years of peace and plenty a good many of them forgot their own true God, and all He had done for them, and turned to idol-worship, setting up wooden images on the hills as the Canaanites did, and praying to them.

Then suddenly, at harvest time, a vast company of men and camels appeared, riding in from the east, and they set up their numberless black tents in the country of the Israelites. These men were called Midianites, and they came to rob the Children of Israel. They took the corn and the olives and the grapes, the sheep and the cattle; and when the people tried to defend their homes and their crops, they fought them and drove them into the hills.

For seven years they did this, until the Children of Israel were almost starving, and hid in dens and caves among the hills whenever the Midianites appeared. Then they cried to God in their misery, and once more He sent them a leader.

Now there was a young man named Gideon, and he believed in God and loved Him. His mind was full of the troubles of his people, wondering how they could be helped.

Suddenly one day Gideon heard a voice: "The Lord is with thee, thou mighty man of valour!" and then he saw the angel of the Lord sitting under a nearby oak tree. And the angel told him that God had chosen *him* to save his people from the Midianites.

At first Gideon was troubled at the thought of this hard task, but God cheered him and gave him courage: "Surely I will be with thee, and thou shalt smite the Midianites as one man."

Now Gideon's father was one of those who had turned from the worship of God and set up images of Baal on the hillside. God told Gideon that his first task must be to throw down those false gods and to build there an altar to the true God.

This was a dangerous thing to do, and could not be done in the daytime. So it was in the starlit darkness late that night that Gideon and ten of his servants crept noiselessly through the village and up the hillside. Each man carried in his hand an axe. Cautiously they crept upwards until they reached the altar of Baal. There they stood still and quiet for a moment, listening. A jackal howled farther up the hillside, an owl flew by on silent wing, but no sound of man disturbed the stillness. But now each axe was raised and brought crashing down on the image of Baal, until it was broken into pieces. Then Gideon and his men broke up the stones of the altar and sent them hurtling down the hillside.

Then they gathered fresh stones and built an altar to God, and made a sacrifice to Him.

Next morning, all the village gathered to see what had been done. Everyone knew that it was Gideon's doing, and the people were very angry. They went to his father, Joash, and demanded that he should bring Gideon out to them, that they might kill him for destroying the altar of their god.

But Gideon's father refused to bring him out. He said that if Baal were really a mighty god he would come himself to punish Gideon. But Baal, of course, did not come; he was only a wooden image. So Gideon was not put to death.

Instead he told everyone of what the angel of the Lord had said, and he called them all to serve the true and living God, who could deliver them from the Midianites.

And the people listened, and soon they knew that God had sent Gideon to be their leader.

The Battle in the Darkness

At harvest time there came again a great army of Midianites, and other people with them, and they pitched their tents in the valley.

73

When Gideon saw them, he knew the time had come to act. He blew a trumpet, and sent messengers to all the tribes, summoning men to come to fight the enemy. The people were so glad to have a leader that they came in *thousands*— thirty thousand men came to follow Gideon.

That was a great army, but God did not want the Children of Israel to think that *they* had conquered the Midianites alone. God wanted them to recognise that *He* was their real Saviour.

So Gideon spoke to the men—he spoke to them of the skill and power of the enemy, of the peril and risk they would have to face in the battle. Then he cried, "Let him that is afraid or fearful go home."

Many of the men were glad to go without fighting, and when they had gone there were ten thousand left.

But God thought ten thousand too many.

Gideon took the men down to a spring and watched them as they drank. Most of them knelt carelessly down to drink, but here and there a man just stooped a little, took up water in his hand, and lapped as a dog laps, still keeping a sharp lookout for any hidden enemy. Only three hundred of the men drank this way. They were the cautious and careful ones. God told Gideon that he would save Israel with just those three hundred men.

That night, Gideon, up on the hillside, looking down into the valley at the vast numbers of the enemy, for a moment felt afraid. But God sent him a sign that all would be well.

Gideon and his servant, Phurah, crept down in the darkness, hiding behind rocks and bushes, until they came near the camp of the enemy. And they heard two of the Midianites talking.

"Behold, I dreamed a dream," said one, "and lo! a cake of barley bread tumbled into the host of Midian, and came unto a tent, and smote it, that it fell, and overturned it, and the tent lay along."

The other man answered, "This is nothing else save the sword of Gideon, for into his hands hath God delivered Midian and all his host."

When Gideon heard that, he fell on his knees and thanked God with a glad heart. Then he and Phurah crept back to the waiting three hundred.

Gideon carefully explained to them his plan.

Each man had a ram's-horn trumpet swinging around his neck and carried a pitcher, inside which was a smouldering torch—only the smoke came out, no light could be seen. And every man went armed.

Gideon divided the three hundred into three companies. He told them to creep silently down the hill and surround the camp of the enemy, and when he gave them the sign, to do as he did.

Quietly they went their way until all around the sleeping Midianites the three hundred stood silently in the darkness, awaiting the signal.

Suddenly a trumpet rang out—Gideon's.

Immediately trumpets blared from every side, crack upon crack rang out as the pitchers were shattered. Three hundred flaming torches were waved wildly as three hundred voices shouted triumphantly: "The sword of the Lord, and of Gideon! The sword of the Lord, and of Gideon!"

The Midianites woke in a panic. Scrambling up anyhow, they rushed every way in the darkness, striking out at anyone they met, not knowing whether it were friend or foe. Camels, terrified at the noise and the flaring lights, trampled down tents and men alike, struggling to get away.

Then Gideon and his men rushed upon them.

And at that battle in the darkness, the Midianites were so terribly defeated that they came no more to trouble the Israelites.

Jephthah's Vow

But alas! The Children of Israel soon turned again to idols, and this time God allowed the Ammonites to come and trouble them.

Now at that time there was a brave and valiant man, called Jephthah, but his stepmother and his half-brothers thrust him out of his home, and the people of his city, Gilead, drove him away into exile. Jephthah found a dwelling place among the mountains and wild regions east of the Sea of Galilee, and numbers of other outlaws like himself gathered to him and made him their chief. And his fame spread throughout the countryside.

When the people of Gilead heard of the advance of the Ammonites, they were very frightened and met together to decide on a course of action. There was no one brave enough among their number to lead them against the enemy. What were they to do? There was only one man who could help them—the exiled Jephthah.

So Jephthah was surprised one to day to see a number of anxious elders from Gilead making their way along the track towards his house. He came out to meet them politely enough and waited to hear what they had to say.

"Come and be our captain that we may fight the children of Ammon," they said. And Jephthah said to the elders, "Did ye not hate and expel me out of my father's house? And why are ye come unto me now when ye are in distress?" And the elders said to Jephthah, "Therefore we turn again to thee now, that thou mayest go with us, and fight against the children of Ammon, and be our head over all the inhabitants of Gilead."

Now Jephthah did not quite trust the elders, and though his kind heart was touched at the thought of the trouble that was coming upon his land, he thought to himself that as soon as he had saved them, they would turn against him again, and despise him as before. So he said.

"If ye bring me home again to fight against the children of Ammon, and the Lord deliver them before me, shall I then be your head?"

Then the elders eagerly swore to Jephthah that if only he would come, he should not only be their captain for one battle, but he should be their head, or judge, for the rest of his life.

So Jephthah agreed to do what he could, and he sought God's help and guidance.

Before Jephthah left home, he said goodbye to his only child, a daughter whom he loved very, very dearly. She was glad that her father should fight for God, but she was also frightened, so she also prayed to God and waited anxiously for her father's return.

So Jephthah went off with the elders, and instantly sent a stern message to the king of Ammon, saying, "What hast thou to do with me, that thou art come against me to fight in my land?"

The king of Ammon was astonished to receive such a message from this unknown man, and sent back a scornful answer that the land he was invading really belonged by right to him.

But Jephthah knew that God had given this land to the Children of Israel, so he sent a second defiant message to the king, saying, "Wherefore I have not sinned against thee, but thou doest me wrong to war against me: the Lord the Judge be judge this day between the children of Israel and the children of Ammon."

But the king of Ammon would not listen to Jephthah's message, and prepared to fight.

Then the Spirit of the Lord came over Jephthah, and as he passed through the land everyone knew that God was with him, and fighting men gathered together to help him.

In his gratitude to God, Jephthah vowed a very solemn vow, and just before the battle started, he said, "If Thou shalt without fail deliver the children of Ammon into mine hands, then it shall be that that which cometh forth of the doors of my house to meet me, when I return in peace from the children of Ammon, shall surly be the Lord's, and I will offer it up for a burn offering."

Then the great battle started, and the children of Ammon were slaughtered by Jephthah's army.

With great joy in his heart, Jephthah returned home, anxious to tell his beloved daughter all that the Lord had done! The girl, however, had already heard the news and went out to meet him, dancing joyously and playing music on the timbrels.

But to her surprise and horror, her father, instead of rushing forward to meet her, stood quite still and tore his clothes from top to bottom as a sign of dreadful sorrow. For, indeed, the moment he saw her he remembered how he had promised to sacrifice to the Lord whatever first come forth from his house on his return.

But Jephthah's daughter feared that her father must have been defeated after all, and as she stared at him, she implored him to tell her what was wrong.

"Alas, my daughter!" he answered her, "thou hast

Gideon watches how the men drink

Jephthah remembers his promise

brought me very low. Thou art the cause of my trouble, for I have made a promise to God, and I cannot go back."

Jephthah's daughter was a brave, noble girl, and she answered quickly, "My father, if thou hast promised anything to the Lord, do to me according to what thou hast promised, because the Lord hath taken vengeance for thee of thy enemies."

How Jephthah loved his daughter for her brave reply! He could not indeed actually slay his daughter and offer her as a burnt offering, but he could dedicate her to God, which meant that she could never marry, and that Jephthah would never have any grandchildren to carry forward his name.

This was a grief to Jephthah and his daughter, but neither of them dreamed of going back on the promise which had been made to God.

So the girl asked leave of her father to go away for two months among the mountains with her companions so that she might mourn over her fate. When she returned, Jephthah dedicated her to God, and she remained unmarried for the rest of her life.

And it became a custom for the women among the Children of Israel to go four days every year to Jephthah's daughter to comfort her, because she could never be a mother and have children of her own.

Jephthah lived six years after this, so when he died his brave daughter felt more lonely than ever, but she had the great joy of knowing that she had not rebelled against her father's vow, and that God himself was her friend.

The Story of Samson

Samson was a giant of a man, tall and broad and tremendously strong—the strongest man who ever lived and one of the bravest. His long hair fell below his shoulders, for he had never had it cut in his life. Before he was born, his parents had been told by God that he was never to touch wine or grapes and that he must never be shorn. For Samson was to begin to deliver Israel out of the hands of the Philistines and to be a leader of the people. That was to be his great task for God.

The Philistines lived in the coast lands, and they were rich and powerful, with cities and temples, and a fair and fruitful land. They were a continual torment to the Israelites, raiding them and robbing them of their crops, keeping them always in terror of invasion. But when Samson came to his full strength, it was *he* who kept the *Philistines* in a state of terror so that they hated and feared him.

Yet though he was so strong and brave, the story of Samson is a sad one. He did many exciting things, yet he did not always act wisely or well, but wilfully followed his own pleasures, only doing his work for God fitfully.

One of the exciting things happened one day as Samson went striding through the vineyards. Suddenly a *lion* sprang out at him! But Samson just seized it with his bare hands, as though it were a kitten, killed it and hurled the body into the bushes. A few days later, however, passing that way again, he turned aside to see what had become of the lion. He heard a buzzing, and found to his surprise that some wild bees had made a home in the lion's mouth and were busily storing honey, though the vultures had pecked bare the rest of the lion's carcass. Samson took some of the honey and ate it.

"Out of the eater came forth meat, and out of the strong came forth sweetness." Samson, amusing himself, made a riddle of it.

As he grew up, he began to worry the Philistines. One day he went to one of their cities and killed thirty of them, and another time he set all their harvest fields ablaze, and their vineyards and olive trees, by letting loose among them three hundred jackals with firebrands tied to their tails.

The angry Philistines tried to take revenge for this, but Samson fought and killed a great many of them, and then went away to a rock called Etam. So the Philistines marched into the Israelite country and demanded that Samson be handed over to them. The Israelites were so frightened that three thousand of them hurried to find Samson.

When Samson heard what they wanted, he allowed them to bind him with new cords and to lead him to the Philistines. When his enemies saw him coming, bound and, as they thought, helpless, they shouted in triumph. But as Samson came into the midst of them "the spirit of the Lord came mightily upon him", he burst his bonds, picked up the jawbone of an ass lying near, and slew a thousand men with it.

Then the proud and admiring Israelites made Samson their judge, and he judged them for twenty years.

But the Philistines hated him, and were always watching for a chance to capture him. Once they thought they had succeeded. One evening Samson went to one of their cities, called Gaza. The Philistines closed the city gates and waited for morning. Now, they thought, they would capture their enemy, for he would be obliged to pass through the gates on his way home. But Samson rose in the middle of the night. When he reached the gates, he just wrenched out the posts and took away the heavy gates, posts, bar and all, on his broad shoulders. He carried them to the top of a far hill, and there he left them standing as a warning to all his enemies.

Now Samson loved a Philistine woman named Delilah, and he often went to see her. So the lords of the Philistines went to her secretly and offered her much money if she would find out how it was that Samson was so strong. Delilah was only pretending to love Samson, so the next time he came she asked him what made him so strong, and how he might be bound so that he would be weak as other men. Samson laughed, and told her that if he were bound with seven green withes, or long twigs such as baskets are made with, that had never been dried, he would become weak as other men.

Delilah told the lords of the Philistines, and they brought her the withes. When Samson came again, there were men hidden in the house, and Delilah, pretending it was a game, bound him with the withes, then called loudly, "The Philistines be upon thee, Samson!" so that the hidden men could hear. But Samson just snapped the withes as though they had been burnt threads. So his secret was still his own.

Twice more this treacherous woman asked her question, and twice more Samson told her nonsense, so that once she bound him with new cords, and once she wove his long hair into the web of her loom and fastened it with a pin. And each time, when she had done as he said, she cried out, "The Philistines be upon thee, Samson!" And each time Samson broke free without trouble.

Then Delilah reproached him bitterly, saying he could not truly love her, and she plagued him with her questions every day.

Samson should have known by now that Delilah was not to be trusted but he loved her very much, and so at last he told her the truth. "If I be shorn, then my strength will go from me."

Then that wicked Delilah sent for the lords of the Philistines and said that now she knew the truth. So they hid themselves, and when Samson came in, Delilah soothed him to sleep against her knee. Then she called to a man, who came and cut off all Samson's splendid hair. When that was done, Delilah called as before, "The Philistines be upon thee, Samson!"

Samson awoke, not at all alarmed. But to his horror he saw his hair lying there on the floor, and knew that he was betrayed, and that now indeed his strength was gone.

The Philistines seized him and carried him away in triumph. They cruelly put out his eyes and made him grind corn in the mill.

Poor Samson, what a terrible punishment, blind and helpless among his enemies! He could only wish that he had always used his great strength in God's service and pray for forgiveness and help in his troubles.

And as the days went on, his hair began to grow!

There came a day when the Philistines held a great feast in honour of their god, Dagon, for delivering them from Samson. Their temple was full of men and women, all the lords of the Philistines were there, and three thousand people upon the roof.

Samson was sent for that they might mock and revile him. He came in, chained, and led by a lad who set him between the two pillars that held up the roof. The blind giant asked the boy to let him feel the pillars with his hands.

Then Samson prayed to God for one last blessing. "O Lord God, remember me, I pray thee, and strengthen me, only for this once, O God, that I may be avenged of the Philistines for my two eyes."

Then, taking hold of a pillar on either side, and saying, "Let me die with the Philistines!" Samson pressed against them with all his might.

The pillars broke, and with a terrible crash the roof fell in!

All the people on the roof and in the house were killed, and underneath the ruins lay that brave hero, Samson, who had atoned for his past mistakes by this one last tremendous deed.

Four Great Leaders

The Child in the Temple

Up through the cornfields and the vineyards, and the fields of flax which were blue as summer skies when the flowers were out, up to the temple on the little hill of Shiloh, came the faithful followers of God to the yearly sacrifice.

Among the pilgrims came a man named Elkanah, with his wife Peninnah and her children, and his young wife Hannah, with their little son, Samuel. Elkanah came every year, but it was some years since Hannah had come with him, for while Samuel was very young she stayed at home. Now he was old enough to come too.

Elkanah had brought three bullocks for the sacrifice, flour and wine also. One of the bullocks was killed, and part of it burnt on the altar of sacrifice, part was given to the priests, and with the rest Elkanah made a great feast for his family. All around were other families feasting too. But while the merrymaking and rejoicing were going on, Hannah took little Samuel by the hand and slipped away to the temple again. For she had something far better than a bullock to give to the Lord. She was taking to Him her little son.

So she brought him to the High Priest, whose name was Eli. And when Eli saw her she said to him, "O my lord, I am the woman who stood by thee here, praying to the Lord. For this child I prayed, and the Lord hath given me my petition which I asked of Him; therefore I have lent him to the Lord; as long as he liveth he shall be lent to the Lord."

And Eli remembered Hannah—remembered that he had seen her one day a few years before, praying in the temple, praying with all her heart for a little son of her own. For she had no children, and it was a great sorrow to her. So Eli had blessed her, and now Hannah had this beautiful little son, and in gratitude she was giving him back to the Lord, to live in the temple and serve Him always.

So Hannah and Elkanah went home, leaving little Samuel with the High Priest. And Eli loved him, and taught him to worship God and to serve in the temple. Samuel learned of the tablets of stone which God had given to Moses, and which were kept in the Holy Ark where the golden angels guarded the Mercy Seat; of the little vase of manna kept there also as a remembrance of the days when God fed the Children of Israel in the desert; and of Aaron's rod that blossomed in the night; and of all that God had done for His people.

And Samuel learned to tend the lamps in the Sanctuary, to fill them with oil and to set a light to the floating wicks so that the flame shone bright and clear, to care for the golden candlesticks and the golden censers for the incense. And he waited on Eli and did all that he required.

Every year his father and mother came to see him, and always his mother brought him a little new coat, which she had made for him, each year a little longer as Samuel grew. How happy those meetings must have been! No doubt as time went on Hannah brought his brothers and sisters to see him, for she had three more sons and two daughters.

So Samuel grew in grace and in strength, and was well beloved. God loved Samuel, too, serving Him with all his heart in the temple, and one night God spoke to him.

The lamps were still burning with a soft clear light when Samuel lay down to sleep in the dusky shadows where the embroidered curtains hung, and nearby Eli lay, with his dim, tired eyes closed. Eli was growing old.

And as Samuel lay quiet and dreamy he heard a voice in the temple calling him, "Samuel!" Samuel answered, "Here am I," and he ran to Eli. "Here am I," he said, "for thou callest me."

But Eli said, "I called not; lie down again."

Samuel lay down, but again came the calling voice, "Samuel!"

Again Samuel ran to Eli. "Here am I, for thou didst call me!" But again Eli said, "I called not, my son; lie down again."

A third time Samuel heard the call, and he ran to Eli. Then Eli understood that God was calling Samuel, and he told him to lie down, but if he heard the voice again, to answer, "Speak, Lord, for Thy servant heareth."

So Samuel went and lay down in his place. And the Lord came and called again, "Samuel! Samuel!"

Then Samuel answered, "Speak, Lord, for Thy servant heareth."

And in the silence of the night God gave to the boy a message for Eli.

Now Eli was a good man, but he was tired and sad, for his two sons, Hophni and Phinehas, who also served in the temple, were very wicked. They were greedy and cheated the people, often taking far more than their fair share of the offerings. They did other wrong things too, which made them quite unfit to serve God and caused many people to stay away from the temple altogether. Eli tried to make them behave better, but though they disobeyed him, he did not send them away, and they continued in their evil ways.

God's message for Eli was a solemn warning against his wicked sons, and his own sin in not having been more strict with them, and of the punishment which would surely come.

It was a sad message for Samuel to give to the kind old Priest, but when morning came and Samuel had opened the temple doors and was going about his duties, Eli called him and asked what God had said. And Samuel told him all. Eli, who knew that he had been weak when he should have been strong, and that it was because of his failure that God had spoken to Samuel instead of to himself, said, "It is the Lord, let Him do what seemeth Him good."

Samuel grew up in the temple, and God was with him, and Samuel learned to know God's voice. All the people listened to his words, and they soon began to understand that God was teaching Samuel to be a prophet and a leader for them. And Samuel judged Israel all the days of his life.

Samuel Chooses a King

There came a sad and terrible day when God's warning to Eli came true.

The Israelites were at war with the Philistines, and the Philistines were victorious. So the sons of Eli took the wonderful Ark of God from the temple at Shiloh, and carried it into battle, thinking that God would surely fight for them if his golden Ark went with them. But God was not with them, for they had sinned against Him. The Israelites were defeated, the sons of Eli killed, and the Holy Ark of God was captured by the enemy.

Eli, old and blind, sat by the wayside, waiting for news. His heart was anxious for the Ark of the Lord.

At last one came running with tidings of the battle. He told him of the death of his sons, the defeat of the Israelites and, worst of all, of the capture of the Ark of God. At this terrible news Eli was so overcome with grief that he fell backwards from his seat, and died there beside the way.

Samuel was full of sorrow at these dreadful happenings. He left Shiloh and wandered the countryside, urging the people to serve the one true God, trying to make them understand that God would be with them once more if only they would turn to Him. And the people listened to Samuel, for they all knew how good and wise he was and how he had served God faithfully.

So Samuel became their leader, and he judged the people wisely. He made his home at Ramah, where he had been born, but each year he went from place to place, teaching the people God's laws and helping them in every way he could.

When Samuel was getting old, he made his sons judges over Israel. But his sons were not good and wise as he was, and the people hated them.

Then the older men of Israel went to Samuel at Ramah and said, "Behold, thou art old, and thy sons walk not in thy ways; now make us a king to judge us like all the nations."

Samuel warned them that if they took a king for their leader instead of God, then the king would do as other kings did—he would take their sons for soldiers, their daughters for servants, their fields and vineyards to give to his followers. When all these things happened, he told them, they would cry out against them, but it would be too late then to call upon God. But the Israelites would not listen, they still demanded a king, so at last Samuel agreed to find one for them.

Now there was a man named Kish, who belonged to the tribe of Benjamin, and one day Kish discovered that some of his asses had strayed away. So he sent for his son, Saul, and told him to take a servant and go to find them.

Saul and the servant set out. They hunted everywhere among the hills and rocks, they asked in all the villages, but found no asses. So after three days' unsuccessful search Saul said that they had better return home.

But the servant said, "Behold now, there is in this city a man of God, and he is an honourable man; all that he saith cometh surely to pass; now let us go thither, peradventure he can show us our way."

Saul thought it a good plan, but said that he had no present to take to the man of God and they could not go without one. The servant told him that he had with him a piece of silver, and they could give that. So Saul said, "Well said! Come, let us go."

They set off to find Samuel, and it chanced that Samuel himself met them. Saul stopped him to ask where they might find the man of God.

Now God had told Samuel that that very day He would send to him a man of the tribe of Benjamin to be ruler. So

Samson presses against the pillars with all his might

David and Goliath

when Samuel met Saul, so tall and handsome—head and shoulders taller than any man in the country—he knew that this was the man God meant him to choose.

And so it was that when Saul asked his simple question, he received a most surprising answer. Samuel told him, first, that he was speaking to the man of God; then, that he need worry no more over his father's asses, for they were found; lastly, most surprising of all to the young man, that Saul himself was the man whom all Israel was seeking.

"Wherefore speakest thou so to me!" cried puzzled Saul in great amazement.

Samuel took Saul with him to a great feast held in the high place outside the city walls, and he made him sit in the chief seat. The people there looked on Saul and thought he would make a fine leader to free them from the Philistines.

That night Samuel and Saul talked for a long time on the cool flat roof of Samuel's house. Samuel told Saul how the people had demanded a king, one who should be a fearless leader against their enemies; he told him that God had chosen Saul himself to be that leader, and that if he were to be a good king and rule his kingdom wisely, he must follow the word of God in all things.

In the morning Samuel sent Saul home, but before they parted he anointed Saul's head with fragrant oil and kissed him, telling him that now he was God's chosen ruler over all His people.

The young man, who had started out to find his father's asses and had found instead a kingdom, went home half afraid. He said nothing to his friends about what had happened.

But when the right time came, Samuel gathered all the people together and presented Saul to them as their king. "See ye him whom the Lord hath chosen," he cried, "that there is none like him among all the people." And the people looked on tall and handsome Saul and shouted joyfully, "God save the king!"

The Happy Shepherd Boy

In the days when Saul was king of Israel, a happy shepherd boy guarded his sheep on the hillside at Bethlehem. His name was David. His father's name was Jesse, and Jesse was the grandson of Boaz, who had married sweet Ruth of the cornfields. David was handsome and brave, and as he led his sheep to fresh pastures, or spent quiet days watching them, he sang in his beautiful voice lovely songs he had made for himself. Many shepherd boys played pipes to their flocks, but David played a harp and made lovelier melodies than any of them. David wore a sheepskin coat and carried a rod and a staff. The rod was a heavy club to defend his sheep against attack, and the staff was a stick to help him when climbing rough hills. He also carried a sling, and if one of his flock strayed, David would throw a stone very skilfully, not to hit the sheep but to turn it back to the fold. His aim was very true and sure. Once in a lonely, rocky place a lion sprang out and seized one of David's lambs. But David ran out after him and took the lamb away and killed the lion. Another time a bear came, and he killed that too.

One day along the road to Bethlehem came an old man. It was Samuel, and in his hand he carried a horn of fragrant oil, for God had told him to seek out Jesse and to choose one of his sons to be the next king of Israel after Saul. King Saul was a brave leader against the Philistines, but he had not always obeyed the voice of God.

So Samuel stood by the place of sacrifice with Jesse and his sons, and the people of the village stood around him. Then slowly, one by one, the seven sons of Jesse passed before Samuel. All were tall and handsome men, but Samuel could not feel that God had chosen one of them. God had said, "The Lord seeth not as man seeth; for man looketh on the outward appearance, but the Lord looketh on the heart."

So Samuel said to Jesse, "Are all thy children here?" and Jesse answered that there remained only the youngest, and he was minding the sheep. Samuel said, "Send and fetch him," so one of his brothers went to call him, and presently David came running.

And when Samuel saw his fine, eager face, he knew at once that this was the boy God meant should be the future king. So there, before his father and his brothers and the people of Bethlehem, Samuel anointed the shepherd boy with the fragrant oil and blessed him in the Name of the Lord. Then Samuel returned to Ramah, and David went back to his sheep.

Now King Saul was often unhappy and sad, and had days when evil thoughts troubled him, for he knew that God was grieved with him. One day his servants asked that they might find someone who could cheer him with music, and one of them told him of David, young and fair and brave and a fine musician. So King Saul sent a message to Jesse: "Send me David, thy son, which is with the sheep."

Jesse prepared a present for the king and sent David to him, and Saul loved him greatly. David played his harp, making music so sweet that Saul was refreshed, and the evil thoughts troubled him no more.

Saul sent to Jesse to ask that David might stay with him for a time, so David became the king's armour-bearer and made music for him when he was sad. Perhaps he sang his own lovely comforting song of the Good Shepherd—"The Lord is my Shepherd, I shall not want; He maketh me to lie down in green pastures, He leadeth me beside the still waters; He restoreth my soul"—which is written in the Book of Psalms.

After a time war broke out again with the Philistines, and David went back to his father's sheep, and King Saul went out to fight.

David Meets a Giant

David's three eldest brothers were with King Saul and the army, and one day Jesse, their father, sent David to take them some food.

Now King Saul's soldiers were arrayed upon one hill, and on the opposite hill were the armies of the Philistines.

David came to the camp and found his brothers, and as he was talking to them a great giant of a man came out of the camp of the Philistines and stood on the hillside in full view of the Israelites. He was a terrifying sight, for he was wearing a suit of armour of shining brass, he carried an enormously heavy spear, and before him walked a soldier bearing a great shield. The giant stood there and shouted at the Israelites. "Choose you a man for you, and let him come down to me. I defy the armies of Israel this day," roared the giant. "Give me a man, that we may fight together."

Now this giant, Goliath of Gath, had come out every morning for forty days and shouted his challenge across the valley. But the Israelites were so much afraid of him, no one had dared to answer him. But when David heard that challenge he was angry and amazed. Why did no one go out to fight him? "Who is this Philistine," he cried, "that he should defy the armies of the living God?"

Now King Saul heard about David and sent for him. And David said to the King, "Let no man's heart fail because of him; thy servant will go and fight with this Philistine."

King Saul thought him much too young to fight this huge man who was a trained soldier, but David told him about the lion and the bear, and said, "The Lord that delivered me out of the paw of the lion, and out of the paw of the bear, He will deliver me out of the hand of this Philistine." So at last the king agreed to let him try.

David was dressed in his shepherd's dress, and had with him his staff and his sling. King Saul tried to put his own armour on the boy, but it was too heavy. David took it off and went down to a little brook in the valley, and chose five smooth round pebbles and put them in his pouch.

Then with his sling in his hand he went out to face the giant. Goliath came on down the hillside, but when he saw David, he scorned him. "Am I a dog," he shouted, "that thou comest to me with staves? Come, I will give thy flesh to the fowls of the air and to the beasts of the field."

But David answered boldly, "Thou comest to me with a sword, and with a spear and with a shield, but I come to thee in the name of the Lord of Hosts, the God of the armies of Israel; this day will the Lord deliver thee into mine hand."

Then David ran towards him. He put his hand in his pouch, took out a stone, fitted it to his sling, and flung it with all his strength at the Philistine. The stone hit Goliath on his forehead, and he fell. Then David took up the giant's own sword and cut off his head.

Then the watching Philistines fled in dismay, but the Israelites pursued and routed them utterly.

David was taken to King Saul, with the head of the giant

in his hand. The king praised him for his great deed and said he should stay with the army. So David was made a captain, and was the hero of every man in Israel.

David the Generous

King Saul was returning victorious from battle, and with him came David, the brave captain who, when he was but a shepherd lad, had slain the giant Goliath. As the army neared the city there met them bands of women and young girls, with musical instruments, singing and dancing for joy. King Saul heard the words of their song: "Saul hath slain his thousands, and David his ten thousands!"

A frown of deep displeasure came upon the king's face as he listened, and from that day he hated David and grew ever more jealous of him. But David continued to behave very wisely in all his ways; the Lord was with him, and all the people of Israel and Judah loved and admired him. King Saul's son, Jonathan became David's greatest friend, with a friendship that never failed. But this friendship also angered the king, and he became David's enemy, and was afraid of him.

One day, as David was playing his harp in the king's tent, one of his fits of rage came upon Saul, and he seized his javelin and threw it at David, but David slipped aside and ran from the tent.

Then Saul called to his son, Jonathan, and to all his servants, and ordered them to kill David. But Jonathan warned his friend of his danger, and told him to hide himself until the morning, and he, Jonathan, would plead with the king for his life. So David hid, and Jonathan went to his father and spoke well of David, reminding the king how his friend had killed the giant and saved all Israel from the Philistines, and of how faithful a servant David had been to the king himself.

So Jonathan reconciled his father and his friend, and David came back to the court.

But it was not long before the king again tried to kill David, and so he fled away. And this time Jonathan was unable to make peace. He and David met to say farewell to one another and to vow eternal friendship, and then David escaped to the hills and took refuge in a cave called Adullam. But though the king had treated him so badly, David himself never hated Saul. Saul was his master, and the Lord's anointed, and the father of his friend.

One night King Saul was overtaken by darkness in the

desert and went into a cave for shelter. Little did he know, as he lay down to sleep, that David and the men who had joined him were watching. David's men urged him to kill his enemy while he slept. David refused, but in the middle of the night he himself crept in and cut away a piece of the king's coat.

In the morning Saul arose to go, but suddenly he heard someone calling to him, and turning, he saw David. David bowed to the king, showed him the piece of cloth and told him what had happened during the night. Then Saul saw clearly that David had behaved very nobly, and he was ashamed and thanked David for rewarding him good for evil. Always, in spite of himself, one part of Saul loved David, but his fierce jealousy always got the better of him, and soon he was again hunting David with all his old hatred.

Another time David spared Saul's life, when he came silently upon him and his servant, Abner, asleep in the camp. David was again urged to kill his enemy where he slept, but instead he only took the king's spear, and the cruse of water beside his head, and crept away.

Then David went to the top of a hill some distance away and cried loudly to Abner, the king's servant, rebuking him for sleeping so soundly that a man could creep in and steal the king's own sword unchallenged.

Once more Saul was sorry and ashamed, and he asked David to return, promising that he would seek to harm him no more.

But David could not trust the king's word, and so he went away, and Saul returned alone.

Years afterwards, when Saul and Jonathan were both dead, David became king. He reigned for forty years, and he made his kingdom great. He took the Holy Tent of God and set it up in a tabernacle in Jerusalem, and Jerusalem became the chief city of the kingdom. And there Solomon, David's son, when he became king, built a most beautiful temple for the Golden Ark of God.

Solomon's Wisdom

When David died, his son Solomon was proclaimed king.

There was peace in the kingdom and good government, so that the people enjoyed their homes and their vineyards and cornfields without fear of enemies. Even kings in far-off lands acknowledged Solomon as their "over-king" and year by year brought him presents of gold and precious stones, silks and embroideries.

Soon after Solomon came to the throne, he held a great feast to the Lord, and the night following God spoke to him a dream and said: "Ask what I shall give thee."

The young king did not take long to make up his mind. He had already found out that it was a great task to be a really good king over such a mighty kingdom, so he said: "O Lord my God, Thou hast made Thy servant king instead of David my father; and I feel as a little child. Give therefore Thy servant an understanding heart to judge Thy people, that I may discover between good and bad."

The Lord was greatly pleased with Solomon's choice, and answered in the vision, "Lo, I have given thee a wise and understanding heart, so that there was none like thee before thee, neither after thee shall any arise like unto thee; and I have given thee that which thou hast not asked, both riches and honour."

So Solomon returned to Jerusalem and went to the tabernacle, and he offered peace offerings and made a great feast for his servants.

But after the feast, as Solomon sat on the judgment seat, two women came before him to ask him to settle their quarrel. They lived together quite alone in the same house, and they each had a little baby.

One of the women now told the king that at night the

other woman had accidentally smothered her own baby, and had crept out of bed and put the dead baby in her arms and stolen her living baby. When she herself woke in the morning to feed her baby, she found it was dead, yet when she looked closer at the poor little thing, she found that it was not her baby at all.

But the minute this woman finished speaking, the other woman, who had the living baby in her arms, cried out to her, "Nay! But the living is my son, and the dead is thy son!"

But again the first cried out, "Nay! But the dead is thy son, and the living is my son!"

All the servants standing round heard the two stories and wondered how the king would find out which woman was speaking the truth. To their astonishment, King Solomon ordered a sword to be brought.

"Now," said he, "divide the living child in two, and give half to one and half to the other."

A soldier sprang forward to do the king's bidding, and tore the tiny baby from the woman's arms.

But when the real mother saw her precious baby seized by the soldier and saw his sword raised to cut it in two, she suddenly felt as though she would rather her enemy had the child than that it should be slain, and she cried out in agony, "O my lord, give her the living child, and in no wise slay it!"

Solomon raised his hand to stop the soldier, and waited to hear what the other woman had to say. There was no trouble in her face, only cruelty, and she said scornfully, "Let it be neither mine nor thine, but divide it!"

Then the king knew which was the true mother, and he said, "Give her the living child, and in no wise slay it; she is the mother thereof!"

From that time Solomon's fame spread through the country and through the whole known world, even as far to the south as Sheba, where there lived a mighty queen.

The queen of Sheba was very wise and thoughtful, and wanted to know a great many things which no one could tell her. And she made up her mind that she would go to this great king and see the wonders of his kingdom, and find out if he could answer her questions.

There was intense excitement in Jerusalem when the queen arrived, for she brought many servants, and camels laden with spices, and gold and precious stones. King Solomon received her in full state and glory in his magnificent palace. He sat on an ivory throne overlaid with pure gold, and descended to meet the queen down six wide steps, on each side of which was a beautiful carved lion.

He took her to see the great Temple and other beautiful buildings, built of stones some of which were as big as a small room. The queen marvelled at the wonderful pillars and walls of cedar wood overlaid with gold, all carved out in lovely patterns of flowers and leaves, lilies and pome- granates. Perhaps he showed her his underground stables, which he had had cut out of the rock to hold some of his forty thousand horses.

Every day there was feasting and gladness, and the queen was amazed at all she saw. In the royal kitchens the cooks used every day tones of flour and meal, and thirty oxen, one hundred sheep, besides hundreds of deer and roebuck and fatted fowls. On the banqueting tables all the dishes were of sold gold, for gold was so plentiful that they reckoned noth- ing of silver.

The queen of Sheba did not forget her hard questions, but asked them all, and Solomon answered every one. And at last she said to him in her amazement: "It was a true report that I heard in mine own land of thy acts and of thy wisdom. Howbeit I believed not the words, until I came, and mine eyes had seen it; and, behold the half was not told me: thy wisdom and prosperity exceedeth the fame which I heard. Happy are thy men, happy are these thy servants, which stand continually before thee and that hear thy wisdom.

Blessed be the Lord thy God, which delighted in thee, to set thee on the throne of Israel: because the Lord loveth Israel for ever, therefore made He thee king, to do judgment and justice."

Then, having given Solomon a magnificent present of gold and precious stones and spices, she returned to her own land, praising and glorifying the God of Israel.

PROPHETS AND HEROES

Elijah and the Poor Woman

King Ahab of Israel looked at the stranger with the stern face and the piercing eyes who stood before his ivory throne in his palace at Samaria, and wondered why he had come. But Elijah, the man of God, raised his arm and pointed to the great temple that Ahab, persuaded by his wife, Jezebel, had built for the worship of Baal the heathen god, and he cried, "As the Lord God of Israel liveth, before whom I stand, there shall not be dew nor rain these years, but according to my word." Then Elijah turned and went away.

So Ahab heard from God's brave spokesman his punishment for leading the people to the worship of idols. For King Ahab and Queen Jezebel had set up great statues of ebony to the sun god in the temple they had built, and Jezebel brought four hundred and fifty priests of Baal from her own country to Samaria. Then she cruelly persecuted all the

113

faithful followers of God, and killed a great many of them. Only one hundred of the prophets were saved, hidden secretly by Obadiah, the king's governor, who himself believed in God. When he heard the words of Elijah, Ahab did not believe them. But when he found them coming true, when day after day, week after week, passed, and no rain, no refreshing dew, fell on the parched land, Ahab was very angry. Elijah must be found. He gave orders to search for him everywhere.

But Elijah was safely hidden—he was living alone in a rocky gorge, close to a clear stream. He had no food, but every morning and evening the ravens brought him bread and meat in their beaks, and he drank water from the brook. But as the days went on, and no rain came, the brook dried up, so Elijah arose and left the country of King Ahab, and went to a city called Zarephath. Near the gate he met a poor woman gathering sticks. He asked her to get him some water to drink and a morsel of bread. She answered that she had nothing but a handful of meal in a barrel and a little oil in a cruse. She was gathering sticks to make a fire, that she might cook it for herself and her son, for they were starving.

Elijah said, "Fear not, go and do as thou hadst said, but make me thereof a little cake first, and bring it to me, and after make for thee and thy son." The poor woman, though she had so little, turned to do as he asked, and Elijah called, "Thus saith the Lord God of Israel, the barrel of meal shall not waste, neither shall the cruse of oil fail, until the day that the Lord sendeth rain upon the earth." The kind woman did not quite understand, but she went and made a cake for Elijah, and found to her surprise that she had just as much meal and oil as before. And it happened so every day; she made bread for them all three, but there was always meal in the barrel and oil in the jar.

But one sad day the widow's son fell ill and died, and she in her grief cried bitterly to Elijah that she had shared her home and her food with him, and he had brought her nothing but misfortune. But Elijah only said gently, "Give me thy son," and he carried the boy up to the loft where he slept. There he laid him on his own bed. Then Elijah, kneeling, prayed earnestly to God for help, and God heard his prayer, so that presently the child stirred again, and life came back to him.

Then Elijah lifted him and carried him down to his mother. He set him on her knee, saying softly, "See, thy son liveth!"

And the happy mother cried, "Now by this I know that thou art a man of God, and that the word of the Lord in thy mouth is truth."

On Mount Carmel

For three years the great drought lasted. The brooks, the wells and the rivers dried up. Day after day the fierce sun blazed down on the scorched earth. Night after night the moon and the stars glittered coldly through the bare trees, and no refreshing dew silvered the brown fields. There was a terrible famine, the people and the animals were starving. It was a dreadful punishment. But still Ahab and Jezebel worshipped in the temple of Baal and blamed Elijah for all their troubles.

At last God told Elijah the time had come to go again to Ahab. Elijah went at once, and he met the king as he was riding out to find water to keep his horses alive. And Ahab, when he saw Elijah, called out, "Art thou he that troubleth Israel?"

But Elijah answered that it was Ahab who had brought all the misfortunes on the people by teaching them to worship idols. He ordered the king to bring the people and all the priests of Baal to Mount Carmel.

When they were gathered there, Elijah spoke fearlessly

to the people, telling them it was time they made up their minds whether they would serve God or Baal. "If the Lord be God, follow him," he cried, "but if Baal, then follow him." But the people answered not a word, for they did not know what to believe. Elijah told them he would show them which was the true God.

The prophets of Baal should build an altar, and lay a bullock thereon, but light no fire beneath. He himself would build an altar and lay a bullock thereon, but light no fire beneath. Then, said Elijah, "Call ye on the name of your gods, and I will call on the name of the Lord; and the God that answereth by fire, let Him be God." And the people answered, "It is well spoken."

So first the prophets of Baal built an altar and laid the sacrifice upon it. Then, while all the people watched, they cried to Baal to send fire. "O Baal, hear us! O Baal, hear us!" All day they shrieked and danced and cut themselves, making a terrible outcry, and all in vain.

At last, towards evening, Elijah's turn came. He called the people to come nearer, and rebuilt an altar of the Lord which had been broken down, and he dug a trench all around it. On it he laid his offering. Then to show the people that he was not deceiving them, he made them drench the altar with water three times, and fill the trench also. After that, Elijah stood alone and prayed quietly to God—he did not shout and rave like the prophets of Baal. "Lord God of Abraham, Isaac, and of Israel, let it be known this day that Thou art God in Israel, and that I am Thy servant, and that I have done all these things at Thy word. Hear me, O Lord, that this people may know that Thou art the Lord God."

Elijah ended his prayer, and everyone stood waiting. And suddenly the fire fell, the fire from heaven, and burnt up the sacrifice, and the wood and the stones and the dust, and licked up the water that was in the trench, lighting up, as it blazed, the awed and wondering faces of the people, and the frightened faces of the priests of Baal. And as the steam hissed and the burning wood crackled, the people fell on their faces and cried, "The Lord He is God! The Lord He is God!"

Then Elijah ordered that all the false prophets should be taken away and killed. And he told Ahab that the fire from heaven was a sign that God would no longer leave the land to the mercy of false gods, but would send rain and dew once more.

Then Elijah and his servant climbed to the top of the mountain, and Elijah knelt to pray. He told his servant to go and look towards the sea. The servant went and returned, saying, "There is nothing!" Seven times Elijah told him to go, and the seventh time the servant returned crying, "Behold, there ariseth a little cloud out of the sea, like a man's hand."

Then Elijah sent him to Ahab to say that the storm was coming. And the wind blew, black clouds gathered, and a great rain fell.

Ahab sprang into his chariot and fled before the valley should be flooded. But faster than the chariot, fleeter than the horses of the king, Elijah the man of God ran before him to the gate of the city.

Naboth's Vineyard

There was once a man named Naboth, who lived in the reign of Ahab near a place called Jezreel. He was a good, quiet man, and he had one very precious possession, which was a vineyard and garden.

It had high stone walls around it, and was cool with the shade of the vines, fig trees and pomegranate trees, and the air was fragrant with the scent of rich spices and sweet-smelling herbs. Naboth loved to work amongst his plants

119

and trees, and to gather his fruit, or to rest there during the heat of the day.

Close to the vineyard was a small palace to which Ahab used to come when he wished to escape from the bustle of Samaria.

One day as Naboth was walking round his vineyard he was astonished to see the king enter through the gateway. Naboth stood still and bowed, wondering why the king had honoured him.

Then as Naboth stood upright, respectfully waiting, the king said, "Give me thy vineyard, that I may have it for a garden of herbs, because it is near unto my house; and I will give thee for it a better vineyard than it; or, if it seem good to thee, I will give thee the worth of it in money."

Naboth's face fell, and he said anxiously, "The Lord forbid it me, that I should give the inheritance of my fathers unto thee."

Naboth knew that it was the law that he must not sell the land, which had come to him from his father and which would belong to his children after him, so he dared not sell it, even to the king.

Ahab knew that Naboth was right in his answer and that even he had no power to force the man to sell his vineyard, so he stormed away in a rage, just like a naughty, disappointed child. He flung himself down on his bed, and turned his face to the wall, and sulked, and refused to eat.

Now if Ahab had had a good wife, she would have come to him and cheered him, and told him how foolish he was to get into a temper because he could not have someone else's vineyard. But unfortunately, Jezebel, his wife, was a very wicked woman, and when she heard Ahab's trouble, she was furious that a simple man like Naboth should dare to stand up to her husband.

"Dost thou now govern the kingdom of Israel?" she cried. "Arise, and eat bread, and let thine heart be merry: I will give thee the vineyard of Naboth the Jezreelite."

So Jezebel took the king's seal, and wrote letters in the king's name, and sealed them with his seal, just as if they had come straight from the king. And in these letters she planned a very terrible plan.

The elders of Jezreel were commanded to call the people together for a fast. This meant that they were to gather together and eat no food, to wear rough clothes, and even to throw ashes over their heads, to show that they repented for some dreadful crime.

The people, when they read the royal proclamation, could not imagine what had gone wrong, nor why they were to fast, but they were still more astonished when they found that it was their good neighbour Naboth who had been found guilty of two dreadful crimes.

Naboth, all innocent of evil, attended the fast, and the elders, not caring to go against the queen, gave him an honoured place where everybody could see him. Then suddenly up stood two wicked men, paid by the queen to tell lies, and they accused poor Naboth of the terrible crimes of cursing God and cursing the king.

In vain Naboth, horrified and indignant, tried to explain and to clear himself. The elders would not give him a chance, and the liars roused the ignorant people to such fury against the innocent man that with one accord they rushed upon Naboth, and carried him outside the city, and stoned him with stones until he was dead.

The queen in her palace heard all the tumult, the cries, and the wild shoutings, so she was not surprised when the elders sent her the message: "Naboth is stoned, and is dead."

Instantly she hurried off to Ahab and cried eagerly: "Arise, take possession of the vineyard, which he refused to give thee for money: for Naboth is not alive, but dead."

So the king rose from his bed and went across the sunlit fields to the vineyard. The afternoon sun was losing its heat, and has he entered the vineyard it felt to him more beautiful than ever—so cool, so quiet, so sweetly scented with the herbs and spices—and, best of all, it was now his very own. He walked about eagerly, examining the vineyard as though it were a new toy, and planning how he could alter it, and spend his riches in improving it.

He thought he was quite alone in the garden, but suddenly, as he turned on the path, he saw a strange figure advancing upon him, a wild-looking man, clothed in sheepskins, strong, fierce, with keen eyes, noble forehead and stern mouth. Ahab stared amazed, then his brow darkened as he recognized Elijah.

Ahab was a wilful but a weak man, and he now cried out furiously, yet with terror in his voice: "Hast thou found me, O mine enemy?"

But Elijah answered gravely, "I have found thee: because thou hast sold thyself to work evil in the sight of the Lord."

Then the prophet gave a message to the guilty king which made him tremble indeed.

"In the place where the dogs licked the blood of Naboth," he cried, "there shall dogs lick thine, even thine; and the dogs shall eat Jezebel by the wall of Jezreel. Him that dieth of Ahab in the city the dogs shall eat; and him that dieth in the field shall the fowls of the air eat."

So the curses fell, and when Ahab heard them, he cowered in terror, and rent his clothes, and fasted, and sought to show God that he was sorry for what he had done.

And God, ever ready to pardon sin, put off some of the bitter punishment for a time. But no sorrow could bring back poor Naboth to his home and his vineyard.

The Mantle of Elijah

One bright autumn day Elijah stood watching a long train of oxen drawing their ploughs across a wide field. Beside each plough walked a ploughman, guiding it with one hand and carrying in his other hand a long pole. With one end of their poles the ploughmen used to scrape the soil from their ploughshares, the other end was a goad to urge their oxen at their work. Slowly the long train passed by, while Elijah silently watched. But as the last plough drew near, Elijah took off his mantle and laid it across the young ploughman's shoulders.

The young man knew what this meant—Elijah wished him to become his disciple and to follow wherever he went. At once he left his plough, said goodbye to his father and mother, and went with Elijah. The young man's name was

Elisha, and God had chosen him to carry on Elijah's work, teaching and helping the people and working miracles, when Elijah should no longer be there to do it.

One day, as they were talking together, something very strange happened. Suddenly between them appeared a chariot and horses of fire, and even as Elisha looked on amazed, there came a rushing mighty whirlwind, and in the fire and the whirlwind Elijah was carried up into heaven, and Elisha saw him no more.

Elisha gave a cry of grief and rent his clothes, but then he saw Elijah's cloak, which had fallen from him, and Elisha picked it up and put it on, remembering how Elijah had once laid it across his shoulders at the plough. From that time the power of Elijah entered into Elisha, and he was able to do the same kind of wonderful work.

The Wonderful Cruse of Oil

One day a poor woman came to Elisha in great distress. Her husband had been a good man, but now he was dead. He had died owing money, for he was poor, and the man to whom he owed it was now threatening to take her two little sons and sell them as slaves. The poor woman wept bitterly as she told Elisha of her trouble.

Elisha was very sorry for her. "What shall I do for thee?" he said kindly, and after thinking awhile, "Tell me, what hast thou in the house?" The poor woman answered sorrowfully that she had nothing but a small cruse or jar of oil. Then Elisha told her to do a very strange thing. She was to send to all her neighbours and borrow every basin, every pitcher, every jug, every bowl—anything that would hold oil. Then she was to go into her house—"And when thou art come in," said Elisha, "thou shalt shut the door upon thee and upon thy sons, and shalt pour out into all those vessels, and thou shalt set aside that which is full."

So she did as Elisha told her, and soon the room in her little house was almost full up with the things they had borrowed. Then the two little boys brought a big basin to her to be filled.

The widow lifted her small cruse and began to pour oil into the basin the children held. She poured and poured until it was full. The little boys set it carefully aside and brought another. She filled that—she filled basin after basin, bowl after bowl, until her little sons' eyes were wide with surprise and excitement, and still she said, "Bring me yet a vessel." At last they had to say, "There is not a vessel more!" Then their mother looked in her small cruse and saw that at last it was empty.

So the widow went and told Elisha, and he said, "Go, sell the oil and pay thy debt, and live thou and thy children of the rest."

What a happy mother, and what happy little boys went to bed that night! For when the oil was sold and the debt paid, there was still plenty of money to keep them all in comfort.

The Little Captive Maid

There was once a little Israelite maid, and she lived in Samaria with her parents, who loved God, and taught their little maid to love Him too. She knew of Elisha, of his wise teaching, and of the wonderful things he could do through the power of the Lord. She was a happy little person.

But one day soldiers of the king of Syria came raiding and stole away the little maid to be a slave. How frightened she must have been! Fortunately she was given to a rich and kind lady, the wife of Naaman, the chief captain of the king of Syria. Naaman's wife was pleased with her new little maid and treated her well, so that soon the child grew to love her mistress and was happy again.

But there was sorrow in that pleasant home in Damascus, for its master, Naaman, that valiant and brave soldier, was stricken with a terrible, painful disease—leprosy.

One day, the little maid, seeing her mistress grieving, said to her, "Would God my lord were with the prophet that is in Samaria, for he would recover him of his leprosy." Her mistress, filled with new hope, asked the child many questions. Naaman and the king were told what the little maid had said, and the king, who was very fond of Naaman, wrote a letter to the king of Israel, asking *him* to cure Naaman of his leprosy, for they did not quite understand about the prophet of God.

So Naaman took the letter, said goodbye to his wife, and set out in his fine chariot, taking with him silver and gold and fine clothing for the king who should cure him. When he reached Samaria, he drove up to the palace gates, and soon the king of Israel was reading the letter. But when he had read it, he was in despair. How could he cure a man of leprosy? Only God could do such things. He felt sure the king of Syria was just seeking a quarrel with him.

Naaman waited proudly, and trouble might have arisen, but there came a servant to the king with a message from

Solomon discovers the true mother

The little captive maid

Elisha. "Let him come now to me, and he shall know that there is a prophet in Israel."

So presently the great chariot thundered up before Elisha's small house. The mighty captain expected Elisha to come out to him, and pray aloud to God, and make a wonderful cure there on the spot. But nothing like that happened. Elisha just sent out a message to Naaman: "Go and wash in Jordan seven times, and thy flesh shall come again to thee, and thou shalt be clean."

Then Naaman was very angry—what were all the waters of Israel compared with his own rivers in Damascus—could he not wash in them and be clean? He rode away in a rage.

But his servants spoke wisely to him and said, "If the prophet had bid thee do some great thing, wouldst thou not have done it? How much rather then, when he saith to thee, 'Wash and be clean?'"

So Naaman turned back again and went and dipped himself seven times in the river Jordan, and lo, his flesh came clean and whole again, like the flesh of a little child.

Naaman drove back to Elisha and thanked him humbly and wholeheartedly, and said, "Now I know that there is no God in all the earth, but in Israel." Then he offered to Elisha all the fine presents he had brought. But Elisha would take nothing, he only said, "Go in peace."

So Naaman rode home to Damascus and the rejoicing of his household. And no doubt he and his wife thanked with all their hearts the little maid whose loving memory of her own good prophet had been the means of curing him. How the little maid's eyes would shine with happiness!

Elisha's Prophecy

Now in the days of Ahab's son, Jehoram, the Syrians came with a great army and surrounded the city of Samaria and besieged it. They would not let the country people in to sell food, nor the townspeople out to buy it, and they cut off what water they could so that at last the starving people would be forced to open the gates of the city and let them in.

But day after day the city held out pluckily, until the people had eaten nearly all the food, and what was left was so dear that only the very richest people could buy it. They ate up all the king's horses except a very few, they ate dogs and birds, and rats and asses. The price of an ass's head was eighty pieces of silver, or four times as much as the traders paid to Joseph's brothers when he was sold to them; and for three or four pints of beans people had to pay five pieces of silver.

But worst of all, as the hunger grew more fearful, the people began to forget they were human, and two women actually plotted together and killed a little child that they might eat him.

When the king heard of this, he rent his clothes and put on sackcloth, knowing only too well that the time had come when he could not ask his people to endure any more, but must open the gates to the enemy.

But before doing so, he determined to send and cut off the head of the prophet of God, Elisha, who was in the city suffering with the rest.

The king liked to pretend that it was Elisha who had brought all this trouble upon him and his people, when he knew well enough that God had sent the Syrians as a punishment for his own wicked deeds.

When Elisha saw the angry king approaching, he rose up respectfully, but was not afraid. Indeed, he cried out boldly: "Hear ye the word of the Lord. Tomorrow about this time shall a measure of fine flour be sold for a shekel, and two measures of barley for a shekel, in the gate of Samaria."

Now a gate was an entrance, while a measure was about three gallons, and a shekel was about twenty-five pence.

The King was leaning on the arm of one of his lords, and this lord answered insolently: "Behold, if the Lord would make windows in heaven, might this thing be?"

Elisha looked the man in the eyes, and said sternly: "Behold, thou shalt see it with thine eyes, but shalt not eat thereof."

Now beyond the gate of Samaria four miserable, starving lepers were crouching. As their dreadful complaint was infectious, they were not allowed inside the city, and the Syrians also would have nothing to do with them, for wherever they went they had to warn people against coming near them by crying out: "Unclean! Unclean!"

So they sat and talked, and at last one said: "Why sit we here until we die? If we say, we will enter into the city, then the famine is in the city, and we shall die there: and if we sit still here, we die also. Now therefore come, and let us fall unto the host of the Syrians: if they save us alive, we shall live; and if they kill us, we shall but die."

So late in the afternoon, in the short Eastern twilight, they went down to the Syrian camp. To their surprise, all was silent. Instead of soldiers' voices, or officers' commands, they heard only the neighing of horses, or an ass's braying. Thinking this strange, they walked on more quickly, peering before them through the fast-gathering gloom.

They reached the first tents. Here, surely, there ought to be some sentry on guard. But there were no sentries, and the tents were empty. They passed forward and peeped into another tent, and yet another, till they found themselves right in the very heart of the camp.

Amazement was in their faces. Was ever such a thing known? Here were tents, horses and asses tied up, rich clothes, gold, silver, arms, everything that a magnificent army could need, and yet there was no man. Even the captain's tent, gorgeously decorated and full of rich treasures, was empty.

Poor lepers! Outcasts from everything beautiful in the world, they had never had such a chance as this. They ate the food and drank the wine, and gathered up silver and gold and clothing from one tent, and rushed away to hide it, probably burying it in the ground. Then they went into another tent, collected more treasures, and hid these also; and as it was now quite dark, they lighted lamps or torches, and wandered about gloating over the wonderful things they had found.

But presently, as they rested a few moments, a new thought struck them. They, outcasts of the earth, began to think of the anguish in the poor, famine-stricken city, and one of them said: "We do not well: this is a day of good tidings, and we hold our peace: if we tarry till the morning light, some mischief will come upon us: now therefore come, that we may go and tell the king's household."

So, refreshed and excited, they hurried off to the gate of Samaria, bearing their flaming torches, and summoned the porters or guards.

"We came," they cried, "to the camp of the Syrians, and, behold, there was no man there, neither voice of man, but horses tied, and asses tied, and the tents as they were."

The guards, scarcely able to believe their ears, rushed off to proclaim this extraordinary news to the king, who had already gone to bed.

He was waked, and rose up at once. Yet, as he listened, he could not quite believe that the story was as good as it sounded.

"I will now show you," he said, "what the Syrians have done to us. They know that we be hungry; therefore they are gone out of the camp to hide themselves in the field, saying, 'When they come out of the city, we shall catch them alive, and get into the city.'"

This sounded so likely that the king sent off riders on five of the few remaining horses, to scout and find out whether the enemy was in sight.

Out into the night they galloped, while all Samaria wakened at the news, and crowded into the streets. Yet even though the horsemen rode as far as the river Jordan they saw no Syrians; but all the way was strewn with clothes and vessels which the enemy had cast away in their terror.

What had frightened the Syrians?

Within an hour or two of the time when God had spoken to Elisha, He caused the Syrians to hear a great noise, as of chariots and horses and coming armies, and they instantly thought that King Jehoram had hired the king of Egypt and the king of the Hittites to come out against them. So the horsemen found that the lepers were right, and that the Syrians had fled away; and turning, they galloped back with the good news.

How anxiously the people waited, thronging the walls, staring out into the distance towards the glorious sunrise, to catch a first glimpse of the messengers!

During the long, hot morning someone shouted out that they were coming. The news ran like lightning from one to another.

"They are coming! They are coming!" The cry rose up, and the weary and half-dying children smiled and tried to clap their hands; and the mothers' eyes brightened as they clasped their shrivelled babes to their breasts; and the brave men who had starved themselves for the sake of the women and the children found their eyes filling with tears at the thought that relief had come. For indeed they could soon tell by the way the messengers galloped, and waved their arms, that all was well.

"Go," cried the king to the lord on whose arm he had leaned, "and take charge of the gate!"

Only a few moments and the mad rush began—men, women, children struggling in one vast, surging crowd to get out—to get food to get water to get gold and silver and precious things from the camp.

And so it came to pass that, just as Elisha had said, two measures of barley were sold for a shekel, and one measure of fine flour for a shekel, in the gate of Samaria.

But when the crowd had rushed by, there was one man lying dead in the gateway trodden to death by the people. This man was the scornful, insolent lord on whose arm the king of Israel had leaned.

Three Brave Friends

In those long-ago days, there was a magnificent city called Babylon. Through it flowed a great river; in its walls were shining gates of brass, and it contained many fine houses, wonderful hanging gardens, and a splendid palace. The king of Babylon, Nebuchadnezzar, had conquered many countries, among them the kingdom of Judah.

So among the treasures of Babylon were many precious things stolen from the beautiful temple at Jerusalem, and inside the walls were many sad prisoners. "By the rivers of Babylon, there we sat down, yea, we wept when we remembered thee, O Zion!" they mourned, thinking of Jerusalem.

Among the captives were four fine-looking boys, princes of the House of Judah, and the king gave orders that they were to be kept apart and educated by the wisest teachers in the land. They were to live in the king's palace, given food and wine from the king's table, and at the end of three years they were to be brought before Nebuchadnezzar that he might discover whether their training had made them of use to him. The leader of the boys was Daniel, handsome, full of the wisdom of God, and, like Joseph of old, able to tell the meanings of dreams. And to those four children "God gave knowledge and skill in all wisdom and learning". So that when the time came for them to be brought before the king, he found them wiser than all the learned men he had about his court. They were young men now, and he kept them near him and gave them all high position and power in the land. But through all this, and in that land of idol worshippers, the four friends remained firm and faithful followers of the God of Israel.

One day King Nebuchadnezzar had an enormous image of gold made and had it set up in the plain of Dura. Then he commanded that all the princes, the governors, and the rulers of the provinces, with the captains and the judges and many others, should gather there, and when music sounded, they should fall down and worship the image.

Now Shadrach, Meshach, and Abednego, Daniel's three friends, were rulers of the provinces, so they had to go too. But when everyone else fell down and worshipped, they three stood upright and did not bow.

The king was very angry. He sent for the three young men and told them that if they did not bow down the next time the music sounded, they should be cast into a burning fiery furnace. How easy it would have been to say "Yes" to escape such a terrible fate! But the three friends looked at the king and answered bravely, "Our God Whom we serve is able to deliver us from the burning fiery furnace, and He will deliver us out of thine hand, O King! But if not, be it known unto thee, that we will not serve thy gods, nor worship the golden image which thou hast set up."

Nebuchadnezzar was filled with fury at this, and he commanded that the furnace be heated seven times more than usual. Then he ordered his soldiers to bind the three and fling them into the fire. So they were cast into the furnace, but the furnace was so terribly hot that the fierce flames leaped out and burned the soldiers who threw them into it.

The King sat staring at the roaring furnace, but suddenly he started up and spoke to his counsellors in fear and astonishment. "Did we not cast three men, bound, into the midst of the fire?" he asked. "True, O King!" they answered.

"Lo!" said the king, "I see *four* men loose, walking in the midst of the fire, and they have no hurt, and the form of the fourth is like the Son of God." Then he went near and called to the three young men to come forth; so they came forth and stood before him, and everyone saw that they were not hurt at all, nor their garments scorched.

Then the king cried aloud, "Blessed be the God of Shadrach, Meshach, and Abednego, Who hath sent His angel and delivered His servants that hath trusted in Him!" and he made a decree that everyone was to honour the God of Israel, for no other god could work such wonders.

Then he promoted those three brave, steadfast young men to even higher honours in Babylon.

Daniel and the Lions

Daniel lived in Babylon, honoured and respected, through the reigns of two kings. Then came a king of the Medes, named Darius, who conquered Babylon and set himself on the throne. Darius was ruler over many people beyond Babylon, so he decided to set over the conquered kingdom one hundred and twenty princes, and over the princes three presidents, of whom Daniel was to be the chief. King Darius soon found out how wise and good Daniel was, and he began to think it would be a good plan to set him over the whole kingdom. But the princes and the presidents grew jealous of Daniel and sought to do him harm. They knew that the king loved and trusted him so much, and that Daniel was such a faithful servant they dared find no fault with him openly. They had to plot and plan.

Now they were aware that Daniel did not worship their idols but prayed to his own true God, kneeling at his open window every day. So they went to the king and persuaded him to make a law saying that if any man prayed to any god or man except to the king himself, for thirty days, he was to be cast into a den of lions. They did not mention Daniel or his God, so the king, unsuspecting, signed the decree. Now according to the laws of the Medes and Persians, once a decree was signed by the king, it could never be altered.

Daniel, of course, heard of the new law and knew how the jealous lords sought to harm him. But he went quietly to his room as usual, and before the open window which looked towards his beloved Jerusalem, he kneeled down and prayed and gave thanks to God as he did every day.

His enemies were watching, and when they saw him kneeling there, they hurried off to the king, and told him that Daniel had disobeyed his decree and must be thrown into the den of lions.

When he heard this, the king was fiercely displeased, not with Daniel, but with himself for signing such a decree, for he saw how the jealous lords had tricked him in order to get Daniel into trouble. All day he sought for some way to save his faithful servant, but in the evening the princes came again to remind him that the laws of the Medes and Persians could never be changed. So very sorrowfully the king sent for Daniel and commanded that he be thrown into the den of lions. But as Daniel, quiet and unafraid, was led away, the vexed and troubled king called to him, "Thy God, Whom thou servest continually, He will deliver thee."

So Daniel was cast into the den, and a great stone was set at the mouth of it, and sealed with the king's seal, and the signets of the princes, so that no one could possibly rescue him.

That night the king could neither eat nor sleep. He grieved all night long, and as soon as morning dawned, he hurried to the den. The stone was removed, and King Darius called anxiously, "O Daniel, servant of the living God, is thy God, Whom thou servest continually, able to deliver thee from the lions?" And from the depths of the den came Daniel's voice, "O King! Live for ever! My God hath sent His angel, and hath shut the lions' mouths, that they have not hurt me."

In the greatest joy the king commanded that Daniel be taken up at once, and when that was done, no hurt whatever was found upon him.

Then King Darius ordered those who had accused Daniel to be thrown to the lions in his place. And throughout all his mighty kingdom he proclaimed the power of Daniel's God, Who could work such marvels, and deliver His faithful servant from the den of wild beasts.

HEROINES OF THE BIBLE

The Story of Ruth

Though there was so much cruel fighting in the story of the Children of Israel, there were also times of quiet days and happiness, when the sun shone on the growing corn, and men reaped their harvests in peace. The story of Ruth is one of love and kindness of heart.

Now there was once a man of Bethlehem named Elimelech, and he had a wife, Naomi, and two sons, Mahlon and Chilion. It happened that there came a famine to Canaan, and there was no food. So Elimelech sold his land and took his wife and children to the country of Moab, where there was corn in plenty. It was not very far away in miles, but to Elimelech's little family it would seem strange and foreign, for the people of Moab were heathens, worshipping a god named Chemosh, and knew nothing of the one true God.

Sorrow came to poor Naomi in that land of strangers, for her husband died, and she was left with her two young sons. Later on, her boys married two maidens of Moab, and Naomi welcomed her daughters-in-law, Orpah and Ruth, and they were all happy together.

After a few years, however, fresh sorrow came, for Mahlon and Chilion died also, leaving Naomi and Ruth and Orpah poor and desolate indeed.

From the hills of Moab Naomi gazed across the valley at the opposite hills of Judah, and her own little town of Bethlehem, and her sorrowful heart longed for her own country and her own people once more, so she made up her mind to return.

When she was ready to go, Orpah and Ruth, who loved their mother-in-law dearly, walked with her for a time along the way. But presently Naomi stood still and told them it was time for them to return. She prayed that God would repay them for their kindness to her and her sons, and she hoped that they would find other loving husbands, for they were still very young.

Then she kissed them both tenderly, and they wept, saying, "Surely we will return with thee unto thy people."

Daniel in the lions' den

Ruth and Naomi

But Naomi still urged them to go to their own people, and at last Orpah kissed her again and turned back in tears.

But Ruth clung to Naomi and cried, "Entreat me not to leave thee, for whither thou goest, I will go; and where thou lodgest, I will lodge; thy people shall be my people, and thy God, my God; where thou diest, will I die, and there will I be buried; the Lord do so to me, and more also, if aught but death part thee and me."

Loving-hearted Ruth was determined to go with Naomi in her loneliness, sadness and poverty, that she might care for her and help her, and so at last Naomi agreed.

The two went on together, and how glad and thankful Naomi must have been to have Ruth's kind company.

When they reached Bethlehem, Naomi's old friends greeted her warmly, though they were shocked at her changed appearance. They were very glad that she had Ruth to care for her.

Of course the two were dreadfully poor and had no money to buy bread. But Moses, that wise lawgiver, who understood how terrible poverty can be, had made a rule that the gleanings which were left after the harvest should be given to the poor.

Now it was the time of the barley harvest, so Ruth went

out into the fields to glean corn for Naomi and herself. People, seeing a strange maiden gleaning, asked questions about her, and soon everyone knew her story.

The owner of the fields came presently to see how the work was progressing.

"The Lord be with you!" he greeted his reapers, and they replied, "The Lord bless thee!"

The master, whose name was Boaz, soon noticed Ruth and asked his chief workman about her. When he had heard the story, he went to Ruth and spoke very kindly to her. He told her to stay with the maidens in his own fields and to follow his reapers, and if she were thirsty to drink from the water drawn ready for his men.

Ruth was surprised at such kindness, for she had been afraid that she, being a stranger, might be driven from the field, so she bowed herself before Boaz and thanked him humbly. Boaz explained that he had heard of her care of, and love for, Naomi, and wished to help her. "The Lord recompense thy work," he said, "and a full reward be given thee of the Lord God of Israel, under whose wings thou art come to trust."

Ruth gleaned all the morning, and she ate with the others at noon, and when she started work again Boaz secretly told his men to drop some corn especially for her. So when she went home at evening she had so much corn that Naomi was amazed.

And when she had heard all the exciting news of the day, Naomi was very happy. She told Ruth to continue to glean in the fields of Boaz, for he was a near kinsman of her husband's, and "Blessed be he of the Lord," she said, "who hath not left off his kindness to the living and to the dead."

So Ruth gleaned all through the barley harvest and the wheat harvest, until she and Naomi had a good store of corn put by. And Boaz watched and prevented anyone interfering with her, and everyone was kind to her, so Ruth was happy.

Now Naomi was growing old, and she hoped very much that Boaz might marry Ruth so that she would know that Ruth would be well cared for and happy all her life. And so it happened, for Boaz fell in love with sweet Ruth, and so he went to the gate of the city and, as another good law of Moses made it right for him to do, he bought back the land which had belonged to Elimelech, and then he made Ruth his wife.

So both Ruth and Naomi were loved and cared for by that good, kind man Boaz. And later on a little son was born to Ruth and Boaz, to Naomi's great delight. They called him

Obed, and in years to come he became the father of Jesse, and the grandfather of King David.

And centuries after, on the first Christmas Day, another little Baby was born in Bethlehem, whose mother, Mary, was descended directly from King David, and so from the gentle Ruth.

Deborah—Prophet and Judge

If only the Children of Israel had been true to God when they reached the promised land of Canaan, He would have subdued their enemies, and given them the land to possess in peace and quietness for ever.

But they grew tired of fighting, and more than once they turned away from God and worshipped idols, and mixed with the people of the land, and copied their evil deeds.

So to punish them, and to seek to bring them back again to Himself, God allowed their enemies to conquer and oppress them.

But when they were sorry, and showed that they repented, God had pity on them, and sent some brave captain to deliver them.

At one time a great king called Jabin conquered them. He took their sons and daughters as slaves, and stole the best of their corn and fruit and vineyards. The people were so terrified that they dared not walk on the open road, but had to creep along in byways and through the forest paths.

Jabin took their spears and shields from them, and even when they went to the wells for water his archers sometimes shot at them.

For twenty years he oppressed the Children of Israel, for he had a great army and nine hundred chariots of iron, and over this army there was a mighty captain named Sisera.

But at last the people cried to God in their trouble, and God always listens when people cry to Him, even though they have done wrong.

The Children of Israel had no king at that time, but there lived in the land a wise and noble woman named Deborah. She was a prophetess, and at certain times she sat out under a palm tree and judged the people, and settled their quarrels and gave them wise advice.

God now spoke to Deborah, so she sent for a brave soldier named Barak, who lived in the north, and whose name meant "Lightning".

Barak came at once to her call, and Deborah told him that he must gather together ten thousand men, and make them ready instantly for battle. God was going to draw Sisera and his chariots and his great army to a wide plain through which the river Kishon ran, and here Barak was to fight and conquer him.

But Barak, though a great warrior, was afraid, for he knew he could get no army equal to Sisera's trained men.

"If thou wilt go with me, then I will go; but if thou wilt not go with me, then I will not go!" he said.

And Deborah answered: "I will surely go with thee; notwithstanding, the journey thou takest shall not be for thine honour; for the Lord shall sell Sisera into the hands of a woman." And Deborah rose and went with Barak to Kadesh.

So away they journeyed northwards and collected ten thousand men. They might have gathered far, far more, but numbers of the Children of Israel were so fainthearted and selfish that they refused to come. So Deborah and Barak returned to camp on Mount Tabor and to get ready for the battle.

But as they passed through the country, a man named Heber the Kenite saw them, and as he was a friend of King Jabin's he sent off a message to Sisera, to betray them.

So by the time Barak's army reached Mount Tabor, and looked eastwards across the wide plain below, towards the sea, they saw that Sisera's army had already collected in the plain.

What a terrifying scene it was, for Barak knew that though chariots were not of much use in the mountains, they would sweep all before them in the plain.

But suddenly God sent down a fearful storm of rain, hail, and wind, and, as often happens in that district even to this day, the River Kishon began to swell and roar, and overflow its banks, and turn the hard, dry plain into a marshy swamp. Then Deborah cried out to Barak: "Up, for this is the day in which the Lord hath delivered Sisera into thine hand; is not the Lord out before thee?"

So Barak and his men rushed down the mountainside, making so sudden an onslaught that Sisera's army fled in a panic. The Israelites pressed forward triumphantly, following the heavy chariots, which plunged helplessly in the bogs and quicksands near the seashore, and were swept away by the River Kishon.

So the Lord scattered Sisera and all his chariots and all his hosts with the edge of the sword before Barak, so that Sisera lighted down off his chariot, and fled away on his feet. But Barak pursued the chariots, and the army, and all Sisera's soldiers fell on their swords, and there was not a man left.

But Sisera turned back westwards, and in his distress he made for the tent of Heber, the Kenite. Heber was not in his tent, but his wife, Jael, who was a friend of Barak's and the poor oppressed Children of Israel, came out to meet Sisera, and said to him: "Turn in, my lord, turn in to me; fear not."

So Sisera thankfully entered the tent, and Jael covered him with a rug. Then he begged for a little water, but she gave him instead some refreshing buttermilk. Before he slept, he implored her to stand in the door of the tent, so that if any pursuer came and asked if there were a man in the tent, she could answer "No".

In that country no woman was allowed to invite a man into her tent, and often a husband would kill his wife when he returned if he found she had done so. But probably Sisera was so desperate that he might have killed Jael if she had not invited him in.

As soon as Sisera was asleep, Jael took one of the tent pegs and a heavy mallet, and then crept softly up to the sleeping man and drove the peg through his temples, and fastened him to the ground, killing him instantly.

A little while afterwards, as Jael watched from the tent door, she saw Barak and his men hot on Sisera's track. Then she came out proudly to meet them and cried: "Come, and I will show thee the man whom thou seekest."

And when Barak came into her tent, behold, Sisera lay dead, and the tent peg was in his temples.

To us, living in these days, it seems as though Jael acted very treacherously; yet we must remember that her husband had tried to betray Barak and his men into the hands of Sisera.

Those were rough, fierce times, and the people had not yet learnt to love their enemies, and to deal truthfully with one another.

Brave Queen Esther

There was once a beautiful orphan girl named Esther, who lived with her guardian, Mordecai, in the city of Shushan, in the kingdom of Persia. Both Mordecai and Esther were Jews living in exile from Canaan.

The king's wife, Queen Vashti, had offended him, so he took her crown from her, and sending for Esther, he set the royal crown upon her head, and she became his queen. She was modest and simple, and everyone loved her.

Mordecai was a servant about the king's palace, and one

day, as he sat near the king's gate, he heard two men whispering together and plotting to kill King Ahasuerus.

So he told Esther, and she told the king, and the two men were caught and hanged. Yet the king and everyone else forgot to thank Mordecai or give him any reward for saving the king's life.

Just at this time the king was making a great favourite of an Amalekite named Haman. He set him over all his princes and servants, and commanded that everyone was to bow low before him as he passed along.

But Mordecai stood straight upright, and refused to bow as Haman went past; for he was of the race of Israel, and the Israelites had been sworn enemies to the Amalekites from the days long ago when they had come out of the land of Egypt.

But Haman knew all about Mordecai and who he was, and he was filled with anger, and began to plot revenge.

So he thought to himself: "I will not only have Mordecai slain, but I will get the king to order the slaughter of all the other Jews who live in Persia."

So he watched his chance, and one day he offered the king ten thousand talents of silver if he would order all the Jews to be massacred.

The king was so fond of Haman that he actually agreed,

and giving him his signet ring, he told him that he might write any orders he liked, and seal them with the ring, just as if they had been written by the king.

So Haman wrote letters ordering that the massacre should take place, and had the letters carried through the length and breadth of Persia by messengers on swift horses.

When Mordecai read this terrible proclamation, he guessed that Haman was really aiming at him, and it was dreadful to think that, through him, thousands of innocent men, women, and children were to be massacred.

So he rent his clothes, put on sackcloth, strewed ashes on his head, and went out into the streets, crying with a loud and bitter cry, right up to the king's gate; and the other Jews wept and fasted, and prayed to God to deliver them.

When Esther's maids and her chamberlain told her something of the news, she was greatly troubled that her kind guardian should be in such grief, and she sent him clothes, urging him to put off his sackcloth.

But Mordecai told her, through a special messenger, the whole truth, and implored her to go to the king and plead with him to spare the people.

At first Esther replied that if she went to the king without being bidden, she might be instantly slain; but in answer to that Mordecai reminded her that she also was a Jew and would not be any safer than the others, and he added: "Who knoweth whether thou art come to the kingdom for such a time as this?"

Then Esther answered bravely: "Go, gather together all the Jews that are present in Shushan, and fast ye for me, and neither eat nor drink three days, night or day: I also and my maidens will fast likewise; and so will I go in unto the king, which is not according to the law: and if I perish, I perish!"

So on the third day Esther put on her royal apparel, and ventured into the forbidden ground of the king's court, fearful, but full of faith that God would take care of her.

The king was seated on his throne, and as he saw her, he smiled and put out his golden sceptre towards her. How Esther's heart bounded with relief! This was a sign that she was safe. So she drew nearer, and touched the top of the sceptre. Then the king said to her: "What wilt thou, Queen Esther? What is thy request? It shall be even given thee to the half of the kingdom."

To his surprise, all she asked was that he and Haman should honour her by coming the next day to a banquet which she had prepared.

The king gladly agreed; and as for Haman, he was so proud and excited that he rushed off home and told his wife and his friends of all his glory, and how the queen herself had honoured him.

"Yet," he added, frowning, "all this availeth me nothing, so long as I see Mordecai the Jew sitting at the king's gate!"

Then his wife advised him to prepare a very high gallows, and to ask the king's leave at the banquet to have Mordecai hanged upon it. Haman was delighted at this idea, and hurriedly ordered the gallows to be prepared.

But that night the king could not sleep, and as one of his servants was reading aloud to him from the court chronicles, he came upon the story of how Mordecai had once saved the king's life.

The king was deeply interested, and he asked: "What honour and dignity hath been done to Mordecai for this?"

"There is nothing done for him," was the answer.

"Who is in the court?" asked the king.

Now Haman was so keen to get Mordecai hanged that he had not been able to wait until the next day, but had come to ask the king's leave that very night. The king was glad to see his favourite, and he consulted him as to what should be done to a man whom the king wished to honour.

Haman thought to himself: "That man, of course, can be no one but me." So he answered the king: "Let the royal apparel be brought which the king useth to wear, and the horse that the king rideth upon, and the crown royal which is set upon his head: and let this apparel and horse be delivered to the hand of one of the king's most noble princes, that they may array the man withal whom the king delighteth to honour, and bring him back on horseback through the street of the city, and proclaim before him, 'Thus shall be done to the man whom the king delighteth to honour'."

The king was delighted with the answer, and cried: "Make haste, and take the apparel and the horse, as thou hast said, and do even so to Mordecai the Jew, that sitteth at the king's gate: let nothing fail of all that thou hast spoken."

Haman was struck dumb with horror at the king's words. But he dared not disobey. He was the "most noble prince", and he it was who had to lead his enemy through the streets and proclaim his honour.

When all was over, he returned to his house in terrible grief. His wife was a poor comforter, and even as they talked together a messenger came to call Haman to Queen Esther's banquet. Haman was in no mood for a banquet, yet go he must.

As the banquet drew to a close, the king asked Queen Esther what was her petition, that he might give it to her, even to the half of his kingdom.

Then Queen Esther cried aloud, as she stood before the

king in all her royal beauty: "We are sold, I and my people, to be destroyed!"

The king was astonished, for he did not even know that his queen was a Jew; and he was so careless that he had quite forgotten about giving Haman his signet ring to command the massacre.

"Who is he, and where is he, that durst presume in his heart to do so?" cried the king.

Then Queen Esther turned on the terrified Haman and cried: "The enemy is this wicked Haman!"

The king rose up in astonishment and in terrible wrath, and went out into the garden to seek to control himself.

Then Haman flung himself before the queen and pleaded with her for his life; but even as he did so the king returned, and by a sign the servants knew that Haman was condemned, and they flung a covering over his face.

Then one of the chamberlains told the king about the gallows that Haman had prepared for Mordecai—the man who had saved the king's own life.

"Hang him thereon!" cried the furious king.

Haman was carried forth and hanged, and Esther was the means, through God, of saving her people and her beloved guardian Mordecai from being massacred.